Enjoy the Ride

Enjoy the Ride

The *Crazy Wisdom* of Uncle Sammy, A Rascal Sage

By Sandia S. Siegel and S. George Green

Downstream Publishing

New York   North Carolina   Florida

SECOND EDITION 2013
20139519

FIRST EDITION published by AuthorHouse 2008

Downstream Publishing, LLC
1213 Culbreth Drive
Wilmington, NC 28405

  a trademark of Downstream Publishing, LLC

Cover painting, *On the Outcloud of My Mind*, by Sandia S. Siegel,

Printed in the United States of America

10 9 8 7 6 5 4 3 2 1

Library of Congress Control Number: 2013951936

Publisher's Cataloging-In-Publication Data

(Prepared by The Donohue Group, Inc.)

Siegel, Sandia S.

  Enjoy the ride : the "crazy wisdom" of Uncle Sammy, a rascal sage / by Sandia S. Siegel and S. George Green. -- 2nd ed.

    p. ; cm.

  Originally published: Author House, 2008.

  ISBN: 978-0-9825873-3-1 (pbk.)

  ISBN: 978-0-9825873-4-8 (ebk)

  1. Green, S. George. 2. Dementia--Patients--Biography. 3. Older people--Psychology. 4. Older people--Attitudes. 5. Biography. I. Green, S. George. II. Title.

RC464.G739 S54 2013

616.83/092

Table of Contents

HAWAII

WHO'S TAKING CARE OF WHO?

THE UNION OF BEAUTIFUL WOMEN

THE JOURNEY HOME

Tripping Over Joy!

What is the difference
Between your experience of Existence
And that of a saint?

The saint knows
That the spiritual path
Is a sublime chess game with God
And that the Beloved
Has just made such a Fantastic Move

That the saint is now continually
Tripping over Joy
And bursting out in Laughter
and saying, "I Surrender!"

Whereas, my dear,
I am afraid you still think

You have a thousand serious moves.

—Hafiz

From I Heard God Laughing, Renderings of Hafiz
© *1996 Daniel Ladinsky and used by his permission*

Acknowledgments

Deep appreciation goes to:

Sierra Faith, whose creative talent and tremendous focus greatly assisted the birth of this book;

Ted Graves, whose friendship and mentoring inspired the completion of this book;

Jerry Daniels, who was my closest friend and whose devotion to friendship was unsurpassed;

Gean Cannon, a great friend and legal consultant, whose clarity of mind and deep moral values enable him to help so many people;

Dr. Robin Seto, who goes the extra mile for her community and is a healer on so many levels;

Baron Sekiya, a wonderful photographer and computer whiz who was willing to assist me any time I needed it;

And Joanne Klein for the excellent design work and formatting.

Heartfelt thanks also goes to so many people

who shared life with Uncle Sammy and me; and all of the women in the "Union of Beautiful Women" and George;

My sister Janet, for her humor, generosity, and trust in me to care for our Uncle;

My beloved sweetheart, Windcloud, whose wisdom, love, and joy-filled living inspire and nourish me.

Foreword

Sometimes a book comes along which turns conventional wisdom upside down and offers an entirely new perspective on a subject thought to be previously explored and conquered.

As Sandia shares her experiences of living with her beloved Uncle Sammy, she, herself, is the bearer of the *Crazy Wisdom* she gained from him. Her perspective, which appreciates and sanctifies her years of caring for this Elder diagnosed with dementia, challenges traditional views of such caretaking as burdensome and enervating. Instead, she repeatedly recounts the joyful, luminous aspects of living with a man who was a profound teacher for her on many levels.

There is no hint of sacrifice or martyrdom in her memories. Quite the contrary, there is an invigorating spirit which pervades her years of service to Sammy, a spirit which continually seeks out and finds the incredible gifts in their time together. Love, recognition, and deep value flow through her stories, stories that cannot help but touch and transform those who have eyes to see and ears to hear.

I consider this little book a critical missing piece in transforming our views, as a culture, toward our Elders, and toward their ever available necessity in our lives and our Wisdom Path. It has been a privilege supporting the birthing process of this transmission.

10 May 2007
Sierra Faith, RScP
Literary Midwife

Preface

Crazy Wisdom is a worldwide tradition found in almost all cultures. The variety of *Holy Fools* and *Unorthodox Sages* is endless, and they all share a talent for using laughter and paradox to turn things upside down in order to see hidden wisdom. Since they are not guided by the rules or regulations of convention, their actions are sometimes incomprehensible, and their generally playful behavior can seem like chaos or nonsense to the ego. Yet, through their behaviors, they awaken us to deeper levels of perception.

Crazy Wisdom responds to the present moment and creates an opening to the truth. These *Wise Fools* expand awareness to any and every possibility. Known for their healing powers and clairvoyance, they have a tremendous blessing force; they shift our consciousness so that there is a gateway into the divine, the absolute.

Crazy Wisdom travels, and can appear in anyone, anywhere: court jesters from the Western European culture, Coyote from Native American lore, Nasruddin from the Middle East, the God-crazy holy ones, called Madzubs, from the Hindu tradition in India, the Baal Shem Tov in Judaism, and Dorje Trollo, the *Crazy Wisdom* master in Tibetan Buddhism.

This wisdom may be found in our culture, seeded within the current epidemic of dementia in our Elders. This is not a commonplace idea, and yet I believe it is one worthy of serious consideration.

In dementia, states of mind can shift rapidly. One thought may seem to make no sense, while the next may be pregnant with wisdom. Perhaps there is a profound healing in being able to look for, and listen to, these gems. Their practical abilities gone, their doing and achieving also gone, our Elders are less burdened by their minds; they can have a more acute awareness of the joy of being. From them we can retrieve many gifts.

With our societal tendency to focus so much on mind activity and practical doing, it is not surprising that these cognitive skills are often among the first faculties to diminish, and almost disappear, in some of our Elders. Divine Intelligence may be tipping the scales by leaning so many away from this imbalance into the direction of presence and open-heartedness.

Perhaps one of the purposes of the phenomenon

of dementia is to have these tricksters bring into our midst surprise, unexpected change, ingenious solutions, cosmic detours, and outrageous laughter, all of which dissolve rigidity and control.

They can bring to us the ability to not take ourselves, and the world around us, so seriously. We can be moved from who we may think we are to embrace deeper aspects of ourselves, which contain magic, adventure, and wonder. We can be turned away from the stress of postmodern life, from the *OW* to the *WOW* in the *NOW*.

Can we learn to journey together with more openness, ease, and deep acceptance of these different states of being? Can our Elders then feel a depth of recognition, an acceptance, and an honoring? If so, the more difficult aspects of aging can be experienced with more spaciousness.

Memory, in some sense, is the enemy of wonder, which abides nowhere else but in the present. Wonder is what happens when we succeed in suspending our customary verbal and conceptual ways of seeing. This occurs in various sorts of transcendent experiences, including dementia. The miracle of moment by moment naked existence prevails without ordinary filters. The present can be deeply experienced.

Not everyone will necessarily have a completely grace-filled experience with dementia. But since so many of our Elders do have these elements of wisdom and presence, we are enriched if we remain open to these possibilities, and can find more ease in the aspects that are difficult.

Could dementia be the neurochemistry of one form of transcendence?

Introduction

Once upon a time civilizations respected and revered their Elders. These same Elders in our culture are regarded as *the Elderly,* often cast away and unseen. As a result, we don't benefit from their unique and savvy perspective.

My Uncle Sammy, an Elder, had *Crazy Wisdom,* a spontaneous and playful adoration of life. My life and the lives of others around him have been made so rich and spacious from his presence. He lived in soul time, in the eternal present, and he retained and expanded his incredible humor and wit with the physical condition of severe dementia. Whether his dementia was due to strokes or Alzheimer's disease is unclear. What is clear is that he contributed radiance and great humor to all those around him, and lit up his own life.

This book is about his *Crazy Wisdom* in the grand tradition of the *Holy Fool,* a tradition of irreverence in service to greater reverence. Uncle Sammy was a true

Divine Trickster. He, in his *demented* state, found great joy in his own foolishness and the foolishness of others. Uncle Sammy had a special knack for revealing life's mysterious truths. He was a messenger from a different plane of reality who playfully tricked us out of fear into enjoying the ride with his wondrous foolishness.

Uncle Sammy came to live with me in Hawaii for the last seven years of his life, after he had been diagnosed with dementia. We took care of each other, and it was a passage for each of us into the next stage of our lives. What is often seen as the difficult burden of living with someone with dementia was anything but that: it was joyful for both of us.

My uncle and I wrote this book together. It began on our refrigerator ... on a white board with tips and quips. The writing of this book added another dimension to our lives together: a creative project constructed out of the stuff of our everyday, ordinary, extraordinary life. It imbued and sanctified our lives with a cosmic slant.

Through all the passages until his death, Sammy was keenly aware of his state of being and of his preparation for passing over. He recognized his leave-taking with grace and surrender. He wanted to make a contribution from his experience to all of us.

This book is a tribute to that very intention, and a celebration of this sweet *Holy Fool.*

NEW YORK

CHAPTER 1

The Beginning

The journey began …
My older sister, Janet, called and said, "I'm worried about Uncle Sammy. He's wandering through the streets of New York and it's dangerous. We've got to do something. I'll contact the lawyer from our old neighborhood."

I decided to call my uncle. When he answered he said, "Oh Susan, I'm glad I called you!" He began to talk merrily as he usually did. It didn't surprise me that he thought he'd called me. He always liked to turn things upside down. He was feeling generally delighted, but also baffled by the fact that his beautiful, favorite bank on Seventy-Second Street, the one with marble floors, didn't have tellers anymore.

When I spoke to my sister again, she revealed that the people working in his building said Uncle Sammy usually went out on the street at 2 a.m. or

3 a.m. walking and singing. The staff loved and were charmed by my uncle and his rascally ways. However, they were also quite concerned about him and often followed him at night to assure his safety. They found that this was the time Uncle Sammy chose to visit his bank. No wonder he was baffled!

Janet went to see Uncle and found he had no money, but he was able to get credit at the two local restaurants where he frequently ate. I really should say *snacked* since he actually lived on ice cream and humor. There was no food in his fridge, but Janet did discover a bit of cold cash in a cookie tin, obviously forgotten.

The lawyer from our old neighborhood and the manager at the bank both recommended a guardianship for Uncle. Later I discovered that the same bank manager, who befriended and seemed so concerned about many of his other Elderly patrons, had listed himself as the beneficiary of my uncle's assets.

Janet initiated the guardianship process. A hearing was scheduled. When I called my uncle, he said, "Come and help." This was a very unusual request from my uncle. So, I planned to honor it and go to New York.

When I got off the phone, I suddenly remembered a dream-like vision I'd had many times in my twenties. It was a vision of Uncle Sammy and me somewhere tropical, near the ocean, smelling the windblown fragrances, and feeling the balmy breeze gently on our skin. Uncle Sammy was in a classic Hawaiian shirt, and I was in a swimsuit, looking out to sea, laughing, and kidding around, feeling very close and happy.

Ever since I was a young child, I knew my Uncle Sammy would "take you on a ride." I don't mean an ordinary kind of ride—wherever you were going in your mind, he'd lead you somewhere else. He'd do it with humor and grace, and you'd always find yourself somewhere you hadn't expected to go. So when I went to New York this time and thought about my reoccurring vision, I wondered if this was a premonition: what kind of ride would Uncle Sammy be taking me on this time?

When I arrived at Uncle Sammy's apartment building, the Schwab House, he was both concerned and excited. Sammy wanted me to help him prepare for the upcoming court hearing. He wanted to rehearse what he would present in court. It was an unusual preparation. We went to Barnes and Noble where we bought scores for many genres of music. At his apartment, our initial research was to discover which song to sing. Of course, Uncle wanted to sing in court, because he sang all the time, everywhere. Uncle Sammy rehearsed many songs, many times, as so many of them were old favorites. We sang for days in his apartment. Of course, he also wanted to try them out in the streets of New York, so off we went walking and singing.

His preparation complete, Uncle settled on a song from Gilbert and Sullivan's *Mikado.* On the day of the hearing he seemed quite carefree. We took a cab to Brooklyn and got out at the Superior Court of New York. We walked up the stairs of a grand building with white pillars and arrived in the courtroom just as the hearing was about to begin.

The judge addressed my uncle:

"Mr. Green, do you have anything to say on your own behalf?"

At which point my uncle sang:

"THE FLOWERS THAT BLOOM IN THE SPRING
　　TRA LA
　HAVE NOTHING TO DO WITH THIS CASE
　HAVE NOTHING TO DO WITH THE THING *TRA LA*
　I HAVE TO TAKE UNDER MY WING *TRA LA*
　WITH THE CARICATURE OF DISGRACE
　WITH THE CARICATURE OF DISGRACE.
　SO THAT'S WHAT I MEAN WHEN I SAY OR I SING
　I WELCOME THE FLOWERS THAT BLOOM IN THE
　　SPRING
　TRA LA LA LA LA LA, TRA LA LA LA LA LA
　THE FLOWERS THAT BLOOM IN THE SPRING
　　TRA LA

CHAPTER 1 • THE BEGINNING

GIVE PROMISE OF MERRY SUNSHINE
TRA LA LA LA LA LA LA
TRA LA LA LA LA LA LA
TRA LA LA LA LA LA LA
TRA LA LA LA LA LA LA"

Even after this superb performance, the judge rolled his eyes and ruled my uncle incapacitated. Uncle Sammy remained in a state of jolly good humor, well pleased with the whole affair. As we were leaving, he said:

"We're all blooming together! Bless the Day!"

The hearing over, my sister and I became my uncle's legal guardians.

CHAPTER 2

True Purpose

Worldly purpose and goals seemed outside the realm of my uncle's considerations. In our family myth, my Uncle Eddie led the way, and the youngest son, Sammy, just *tagged along.* It was Uncle Eddie who started the family business, a pharmaceutical company. He was a chemist, very important in an immigrant Jewish family that valued education and being *smart,* i.e., having logical intelligence. However, Uncle Sammy knew his true purpose, his *job,* in the most important sense. The more time I spent with him, the more I understood his real work as well.

As we journeyed through New York, I pieced together, like a quilt, the essence of his life and the lives he touched. At first, the Schwab House seemed to be my uncle's headquarters. But after being in New York with him, I realized that the entire upper westside neighborhood was his territory.

We'd take walks down Broadway. That famous avenue was close to his apartment building, and everyone and everything was there: a potpourri of life. He would be grinning ear to ear, and absolutely didn't know or care which direction we went, or for how long. On one of our walks I asked him, "Uncle Sammy, how does it feel to not be able to change your own clothes, or remember where you live?" He replied, "I have no quality control, only God's nature!" and he was absolutely right. Even then, he knew how to flow with all of life's changes. He was in the eternal present. This state was so different from my usual state of ordinary consciousness. It was contagious, and I was in the Eternal Present with him. It was at this time I somehow knew we had to write this book together. When I checked with Uncle Sammy, he said, "Hell, yes!"

Uncle Sammy exuded so much innocent confidence that he could walk up to anyone and sing or say something unusually relevant: amazing, since they were all strangers until that very moment. I saw, for example, CEOs and street people shift and go from being *guarded* to being *off guard,* open to this extraordinary experience.

He would say:

"I want to make people happy, healthy, and

dangerous. My job is to get people to know they are more important than they think they are."

I wanted to know how he perceived his experience. What was it like for him not having all the normal orientations of time, space, and personal identity that most people have? When I asked him about this he said, "I'm on the outcloud of my mind and enjoying it," and he was. Joy emanated from within him as he said, "It's *all* all right, you know."

In the Schwab House, he brought merriment and music to the otherwise monotonous job of the elevator operators. He had *chutzpa* and a beautiful voice, and he still had a good memory for melodies and lyrics. He could invent songs on the spot as a way of celebrating each person's soul. With a man from Puerto Rico, he sang songs from *West Side Story,* or made up songs in his own kind of Spanish. Because he was so good-humored and respectful, he never offended this man. Another operator, who was rather solemn, lit up when Uncle sang riffs from Gilbert and Sullivan tunes, especially if Uncle Sammy ad-libbed. This gave the man an opportunity to be the *expert.* The man would laugh and then correct Sammy. Uncle would accept the corrections good-naturedly and then continue.

My uncle had an especially good time with a gentleman who was an opera buff, because they could sing duets together, their voices resounding up the elevator from floor to floor. What tickled me most was Uncle getting some of the younger operators going. He loved to imitate their new musical styles. Uncle Sammy *rapping* was simply hilarious.

There was a McDonald's in Sammy's neighborhood, which he exalted and called the "golden palace." There he was known and loved amongst the street people who frequented this palace. I often watched one despondent, Elderly gentleman come to life when my uncle made his morning rounds. Several other people would call out to him to come to their table; different ages, different races, all sharing the common yearning to connect, to feel included. This was his gang: an unorthodox cast of characters.

Banks were his favorite hangouts. He enjoyed lighting up these otherwise somber institutions. Although he was well-known in several banks, Chase Manhattan was his absolute favorite. We frequented Chase on a daily basis, where he created two *jobs* for himself. His first *job* was to approach each one of the women tellers, sing to her, and then, in some way, let her know she was beautiful. They all adored him.

His second *job* was holding the door open for patrons of the bank and offering greetings of wise sayings:

"Trust the way things are; it's the only way to be!"

"The world all works together all the time, so it's really all right, you know."

One winter morning I was astounded when Uncle Sammy had the bank manager, the staff, and many of the patrons joining him in a rendition of "Are You Lonesome Tonight?"

Uncle Sammy had his own *company*, a mysterious company that everyone was very happy to join. My uncle had been the head of public relations and marketing for the more serious family pharmaceutical company until he retired. But everyone in his new company was invited to be the *boss* and to engage in the two major activities of his new company: singing and repartee. One day a friend of mine called us. Uncle answered and said:

"I'm so glad we called you! You will be an amazing asset to our company."

Then he began to sing her praises, literally! He was so engaging that our friend delightedly started to sing his praises in response. She had never believed herself capable of anything so spontaneous.

My uncle befriended any and all he encountered, and was a source of laughter and light to many. Though clinically and legally he was considered completely *incompetent*, in his incompetence, and perhaps because of it, he fulfilled his true purpose beautifully.

CHAPTER 3

Traveling Light

Even as a young child, my Uncle Sammy seemed to me to be an unusual adult. He was always ready to lighten up any situation. Whenever there was an argument between my grandparents and any of their children, he would interject humor. My grandmother, who was very stern, would resist laughing as hard and long as she could, but she could never resist my uncle. I was always curious to see how long it would take him to get her laughing.

During the *high holidays* I was especially delighted by my uncle's antics. Paradoxically, my grandparents, who were atheists, always took the Jewish holidays very seriously and tried to be somber: not easy with my uncle present. He disrupted heavy moods easily and naturally. Since he was seen as a *meshugener* (a crazy person), he got away with it and got everyone laughing. Jesters and *meshugeners* are somehow able to bend the rules.

I also remember Uncle Sammy's love of music. I would slip out of the subdued atmosphere in the rest of my grandparents' house and into the front sunroom, where my uncle would be listening to music on his radio. He and his room were definitely the sunniest and lightest influences in their house. I would sit on his bed listening to jazz, blues, show tunes, and opera. Uncle Sammy would wink at me, so I knew it was all right, and we both would be absorbed in the music. I knew he loved music, but not until he had dementia did I realize how completely devoted he was to the *joy* of music.

He was also unusual about owning pretty much anything. He didn't have the usual yen for material possessions and so had few possessions. This sometimes affected his romantic liaisons. A couple of potential girlfriends, while charmed by his personality, felt embarrassed to be seen with him because he was so out of style and never had the *proper attire*.

As a child, I noticed he would be curious about everything, but almost never bought anything. This remained true during his entire lifetime. As an adult I sometimes would go into stores with him. He'd be fascinated, yet still wouldn't buy anything, even if I offered to buy it for him. He just wouldn't want it. He liked to travel light.

Because of anti-Semitism, both my uncles and my mother changed their last name from Goldstein to Green in order to get jobs. Uncle Sammy changed from Sammy Goldstein to S. George Green. Though he knew the difficult circumstances that necessitated this change, he made light of the change and offered no resistance. He was not attached or possessive, even to his name and his identity, as such.

As an adult, even his refrigerator had very few items. It barely contained any food at all, if you could even call it that. At any given time, one might find some cookies, ice cream, a bit of *cold cash,* and little more.

When Sammy developed dementia, I saw him let go of all practical concerns. He was surfing the light realms. He began naturally leading other folks to those dimensions.

My uncle lived life the way accomplished *Yogis* live—desires, longing, despair did not enslave him. He seemed free from worry and desire for worldly things and ever so joyful. There was lightness in his being, an easy complete acceptance of all current conditions.

CHAPTER 4

The Deli

While I was in New York, I wanted to eat typical New York food. So Uncle Sammy and I went to a deli. All the staff in this deli seemed grumpy: pure grump. From the looks of them they had worked unhappily at the same place for many years.

Though Sammy often seemed not to notice his surroundings, he had a keen awareness. We had finished eating but hadn't received the check yet. Suddenly, Sammy jumped up and started walking towards the door. I scurried after him. All the help in the restaurant were right behind us, united in their attempt to catch this rascal. As soon as we reached the street, he turned unexpectedly and said to his pursuers:

"I was wondering if you were on your toes."

Then he marched back into the restaurant to pay the bill. At first the staff seemed perplexed. Then they started laughing and kidding with each other. The whole atmosphere had lightened up in response to an out-of-the-ordinary practice, a little harmless mischief.

I knew enough not to ask him for an explanation. Had he forgotten, or was this his kind of *fooling around?* He was so innocent—a total *fool* who was not so foolish.

CHAPTER 5

A World of Beauty, World of Despair … Our Lineage

My grandparents, on both sides of the family, escaped from the Pogroms in Russia in the early years of the 20th century. Czar Nicolas ordered Cossack soldiers to go into *shetls*, villages of Jewish people, to pillage, rape, and murder the inhabitants. It was with this history that my grandparents came to Ellis Island in New York City. They were all in their twenties, poor refugees who spoke Yiddish, a little Russian, and no English.

As a child, I knew little of their history, as they never spoke of it. But I could feel the atmosphere in which they still lived: they wanted to forget. My grandparents were very fearful people who didn't trust life, God, or anyone else. For them, the religious

Sammy and Lena

and spiritual dimensions were nonexistent. And, if they had verbalized their beliefs, they would have considered themselves ethnically Jewish, though atheists. They did not believe God existed because they had experienced so much cruelty and terror. The harshness of their early life had left a deep imprint of suspicion and despair. They had barely escaped from Russia, and in Russia they had barely survived.

I knew my grandparents and their home well. We lived near them in the Bronx. In fact, I could leave my apartment building, go through some alleyways, and reach their house in a matter of minutes.

My grandmother Lena started working at age five as a seamstress, and as a result, by adulthood, she could hardly see. The adults in our family spoke Yiddish to each other, but I was not taught Yiddish, and was, therefore, excluded from these conversations. Since much was kept hidden, I only learned about the terrible Czar Nicholas because my grandmother had a dog named Nicky. I was curious about his name. I asked and asked until my grandmother finally said:

"He's named after the czar, who was such a dog."

Even the humor in our family had a dark edge. There was an aura imbued with sadness, a mysterious existence that was not to be revealed.

It was as an adult, years after my grandparents

had both died, that I had my most powerful dream. It was more than a dream: it was an experience of our family lineage and of liberation. My grandfather came to me, and he was a luminous spirit, so real I could smell his scent. That scent stayed with me for days, long after the night of the dream. In the dream he communicated to me that I was loved and cherished. He wanted to release me into the truth of knowing that I would always belong—belong to him and to my other ancestors—so that I could live my own life autonomously and freely. He let me know that I didn't have to carry their history, or the burden of their anguish and suffering, and yet I still belonged. I felt liberated, freed.

After this beautiful communion, he hugged me. I felt his hug with such power that I could literally feel the warmth and the sense of his arms wrapped around me. This feeling was sustained for a long time, for days and days after the night of the dream.

Reflecting on this experience, I felt that my grandfather's spirit came to bring me this gift. And I was, and am, filled with gratitude.

Of the four children in a family with so much despair, only my Uncle Sammy had been able to transmute this despair in himself, and then had been able to transmute this in so many other people. Only my uncle, the youngest, carried lightness of spirit. Miraculously, he had been even more capable of this in the last years of his life when he was so *incapacitated,* so *demented.* He exuded divine joy and laughter: he was *riddled* with it.

My uncle and my grandfather's spirit really taught me about liberation.

CHAPTER 6
Tiger Til

My mother, "Tiger Til," was Uncle Sammy's only sister. He was eleven years younger, and she was as fond of him as if he were her child. She helped raise him. They shared a bedroom, and actually shared a bed, until he was pre-adolescent and she was twenty-one. When he was sick, she took care of him and would rub his feet to comfort him. Her favorite statement about him was, "Sammy, he's such good company." They remained close throughout their entire lives.

My mother had a tough persona. She would say, "Nobody ever tells me what to do." Sammy was light and funny. Though they were of different temperaments, they both had great humor.

When my mother was in her mid-eighties, she became very ill and was forced to have a serious operation. Being in a hospital and having tubes down her throat made her angry. She gave the hospital staff a hard time, and I was quite concerned about the care she would receive with her attitude. Uncle Sammy came to the rescue and solved the problem. When he went to visit her, he told the staff, "That's my sister, Tiger Til." From that moment, everything changed. They stopped taking her behavior personally and understood that this was her nature. From then on she was treated with respect. They understood that she was a person with a strong nature, who was just having difficulty as she aged, and her health and other faculties diminished.

My mother then had a series of operations. After coming out of anesthesia after a third operation, she was transformed: she saw herself as someone loved by the entire world. Initially, she was put into a room with several other women. One was a ninety-nine-year old African-American woman, and she and my mom became best friends. My mother called her "Ninety-nine" and she called my mother "Better than Jesus." They both had mellowed over the years, but could recognize a fellow rascal, and they loved to kid and play together. Ninety-nine was delighted that my mother thought the whole world was in love with her, and that is how she named her Better than Jesus. As fellow rascals, they enjoyed seeing people's reactions to their names. Once again, humor was the saving grace.

And my mother was absolutely right: the whole world *did* love her. People responded to her just the way that she saw herself. She was filled with joy and impish vitality. She livened up the place. The staff got a big kick out of either flirting with her or helping her to flirt. One nursing assistant often helped my mom to dress, and would ask, "So who you after today, darlin', the rabbi, the doctor, or the new man in room five?" This assistant helped Tiger Til put on all her jewelry at once, "cause that is how she likes to dress."

My uncle got a big kick out of her sassy, self-loving transformation. Nearly all of the women in his family became outrageously eccentric after developing so-called dementia. His own eighty-year-old mother would periodically walk to the local pool hall and strip for the patrons. Like Til, my grandmother experienced a radical shift in consciousness in her later years. In fact, many of our relatives developed so-called dementia, and they all seemed to be having a better time of it: not taking themselves so seriously and becoming altogether outrageous.

Uncle Sammy saw my mom enjoying her new state of mind, therefore living comfortably at the nursing home. However, he made it clear to me that being in a place like that would be very uncomfortable for him. He always joked about this subject, but I knew he was absolutely serious.

Perhaps Uncle Sammy had a penchant for older women since he had such a close relationship with his sister, Tiger Til. They shared a pact of humorous irreverence and a deep enjoyment of each other.

CHAPTER 7

Letters

I knew Uncle Sammy had once been married to a woman named Evelyn but not for very long. He didn't seem to be the marrying kind. He did have a girlfriend for forty years named Frances, until he came to live with me in Hawaii. He lived on the west side of Manhattan and she lived on the east side of Manhattan, and they both liked it that way: just not the *marrying kind,* either of them.

I became, as Uncle Sammy saw it, his "guaranteed commander," also known to the legal system as his legal guardian. When I was preparing to have my uncle move to Hawaii with me, I had to take care of all the practical matters for this move of a lifetime. I joked about this, and asked, "Uncle Sammy, can I give you back some of your worries?" He said, "Absolutely not. Don't worry, I never do," something akin to Meher Baba's saying, "Don't worry, be happy."

Before long I was going through mounds of many years of papers. When I found personal notes or letters, I would consult him. How did he want to handle these, I'd ask, "Do you want to keep this?" or "Do you want to reply?"

Amongst these, we read many letters from his ex-wife, Evelyn, and I began to get a sense of their relationship. Apparently, over many years, he sent her and her children vitamins from his pharmaceutical company. The letters were very congenial, and Evelyn often thanked my Uncle for his kind words and hilarious humor. Sammy thoroughly enjoyed rereading her letters, and we would begin many letters to her, but just begin.

Once we reached Hawaii and were at home, we finally sent some of those letters to Evelyn. One began:

> "Dear Evelyn, I am glad you are alive and aware. I donate my happiness to you. I'm just the way I've always been, sooo sexy. Love, Sam."

In the next one he offered to send her thousands of dollars. Since he had notes in his wallet that read that he had various large amounts of money coming to him (S.G.G. gets 41.5 MILLION DOLLARS), he felt generous. He wanted to send her some of his wealth.

Sammy sent these offers to other people, as well. I don't think these letters ever reached Evelyn or any of his other old friends because we never received any replies.

But perhaps the good intentions did reach. They definitely reached Uncle Sammy. He felt great writing these letters, and I could see a glow. These letter-writing sessions lit him up.

CHAPTER 8

Uncle Sammy's Doctor

The veil between eccentricity and dementia is thin …

Some years before any family concern about my uncle, I called him from California. I was missing Sammy. We hadn't seen each other for a long time. I had just returned from living in Latin America, and had come back to the States sick with amoebic dysentery. He answered my call with, "Susan, I'm so glad I called you!" As usual, he thought he had called me.

He was in his usual jolly mood and asked how I was. I told him I wasn't well. I surprised myself by saying this because as an adult I handled my own health problems and did not share them with my family.

My uncle surprised me back by saying, "Come to New York right away and consult with my doctor.

He's the best. I'll send you a ticket," and he abruptly hung up.

Within a surprisingly short time a ticket arrived in the mail. I called Sammy, reminded him of my travel dates, and asked him to make arrangements for me to see his doctor. He said, "Good. You'll consult my doctor. He can cure anything," and hung up again. The hanging up was not out of the ordinary but the solicitous concern was. I had not experienced this from Uncle Sammy since my childhood.

So I flew to New York. I was interested in seeing his doctor. My uncle rarely went to doctors. He was amazingly apt in using common sense to diagnose and heal family ailments.

When I arrived in New York, I went to my friend's apartment where I would be staying, and called my uncle. He was not in. I tried several times to reach him by phone during the first couple of days, but was always unsuccessful. I also went to his apartment building but missed him there as well. I was disappointed and concerned that I might leave New York without ever seeing Uncle Sammy or his amazing doctor.

Finally I came home one afternoon and checked my friend's message machine, as I had been doing each day. Sure enough, there was a message from Sammy. He said, "Susan, my doctor's on right now.

Call him up. He will help you. He can cure anything, if anybody can." At that moment I put it all
together: my uncle's doctor was a doctor who had a
call-in radio show. There was no mention of a station,
a time, or even the doctor's name. I was startled,
and then I started laughing and said to myself, "My
Uncle … What will he come up with next? He's such
an eccentric!"

Eventually I reached Sammy, and we visited a
few times before I was to return to California. He
was upset with me, which was a rare occurrence. He
was unable to understand how I hadn't received the
medical attention I'd come for. I never imagined that
my uncle's doctor was on the radio, and he never
imagined that I'd come to New York and not consult
with this incredible man. After I left it took a few
phone calls, initiated by me, to return us to our nor-
mally harmonious, loving connection.

For some time I was perplexed about this episode.
Although I had always considered my uncle to be
outside the ordinary, I had never thought of him as
having dementia. He simply lived in another world,
and I was usually drawn into that world in delightful
ways. However, this time our worlds interfaced in a
manner that created upset and confusion.

CHAPTER 9

Uncle Sammy on the Run

Uncle Sammy was an escape artist. After the guardianship hearing, my uncle had twenty-four-hour caregivers from whom he was always trying to escape. My sister Janet installed new locks on the door of Uncle Sammy's apartment so he couldn't go wandering off by himself at all hours, as he had been doing. She asked his various house-keepers to accompany him when he went out. Often, after the locks were installed, one could find Uncle on a chair trying to undo the locks and find his way to freedom. He did not take kindly to being restricted or followed.

When I arrived back in New York, my sister was at her wit's end. She had hired someone from an agency, in need of a job, with no previous care-giving experience, glad for any job. From the interview, it sounded to my sister like this man would work out. But as soon as he started the job, he was also at *his* wit's end. He had never as much as met someone with dementia.

Trying to escape this newly established prison, Sammy developed more elaborate strategies. He placed a chair up against the front door of his apartment and gathered and stacked many pillows on top of the chair. Then, having already found some small tools collected from around his apartment, he climbed up. From that pinnacle, he attempted to undo the many locks and escape. Upon seeing this, the new caregiver panicked and pulled my uncle from his homemade scaffold. Given their relative sizes and strengths—my uncle, fragile, under five feet tall and slight of build, and this man, well over six feet and very muscular—the caregiver unwittingly injured Sammy. In trying to prevent Uncle from escaping, he had injured him. The caregiver felt horrified and quit immediately.

At this stage of his life, my uncle's skin was thin and fragile. Given this condition his injuries were relatively minor. He had a few scratches and his wrists were all black and blue.

After seeing my uncle, I told Janet we had to let this person go, not knowing he had already quit. I had a sinking feeling, and I thought this might be the beginning of a very difficult and dangerous time for Sammy. My sister, due to her health, would not be physically present and unable to oversee his care.

Soon after that incident, Janet hired two women who had experience as caregivers. My sister, noticing Uncle's strong desire to leave his apartment, now gave the new caregivers instructions to accompany him on walks but to never, *absolutely never,* let my uncle go wandering in the streets unattended. She, his doctor, and the court considered him a danger to himself.

I went home to Hawaii briefly and, upon returning to New York, went straight to Sammy's apartment. When I arrived, no Sammy and no housekeeper. I let myself in. A short time later his housekeeper arrived saying she had gone for a walk with my uncle. Apparently Sammy had ditched her. After walking several blocks, with her racing to keep up with him, he had given her the slip. Though he was tiny, he was famous in our family for being a brisk walker. And this time he had the added incentive of getting rid of this woman. For some time he had used various tactics to get out of being *under surveillance*. He obviously wanted to still be free to come and go as he pleased. She reported that he had suddenly hailed a taxi, jumped in, and took off and away from her. I was just as concerned as she was, knowing Uncle Sammy couldn't give his name, or his address, or any other practical information, for that matter.

I called the police. I was surprised how quickly they arrived, New York being such an enormous city. They listened to what had happened and told me to get into their squad car and we would look for him around the neighborhood.

As soon as we were cruising the streets of New York, one of the policemen turned to me and said. "Lady, I've done this many times, and how much do you want to bet that by the time we've cruised the neighborhood and returned to your uncle's building, he'll be sitting in the lobby?" Sure enough, when we returned to the Schwab House, there was my uncle, laughing and chatting in the sumptuous lobby with marble floors to the man at the desk. He had appeared shortly after we left to go searching for him. The staff in the lobby didn't seem at all surprised, as they knew his whimsical, magical ways.

How he arrived back home remained a mystery.

CHAPTER 10

An Ordinary Hero

My uncle's swanky apartment building on Riverside Drive became even swankier over the years. Uncle Sammy's apartment was the exception, even though it was a penthouse apartment, 18 Penthouse East. Sammy didn't buy anything new until the old one wore out, and didn't fix anything unless it really didn't work. That, in a way, was how my uncle became my sister's hero.

Janet and I went to visit him together. We knocked on the door; the caregiver answered. My sister went into his bathroom. The door jammed shut, and she was locked in. I slipped a copy of the New York Times under the door and said, "Maybe this will help you relax while we try to free you."

The caregiver and I tried to unjam the door for some time using WD-40, screwdrivers, and small tools that we found around the house but to no avail.

There was an intercom and a repair crew that worked in this elegant, very upscale apartment building. So we called for help. Since this was during the day, we were sure someone would arrive shortly. But no one came, although we called again and again.

Forty-five minutes later, my sister was panicking; still no help. All of a sudden, Sammy, who had seemed, until now, totally incapable of offering any practical help, went into action. In a clear, strong, authoritative voice, he called through the intercom and said that there was a very ill woman locked in the bathroom. He *insisted* on an immediate rescue. Within minutes there were two janitors at our door, and my sister was released from the bathroom very quickly.

To our total amazement, Uncle Sammy had been able to act swiftly and decisively, responding to what the situation really required. He was our hero of the day. Our roles reversed; he rescued his guardian.

Over the years, my uncle repeatedly rose to the occasion. Even when he seemed to be in another dimension, he would notice situations that required attention. And when necessary, he could shift from the cosmic realms and take effective action in the practical world.

HAWAII

CHAPTER 11

Journey to Hawaii

"Hell, I'm ready for anything!" That was my uncle's answer every time I asked him to come with me to Hawaii. I knew he wasn't getting the best care in New York, and I wanted him to be with me.

So we went to Hawaii; it was an experiment. Since my uncle had lived in New York his whole life, we planned to have him come for only a short visit and see if he could make Hawaii his new home. Even though he was eighty, his physical health seemed fine. As we walked the streets of New York, I had to run to keep up with him. We packed a few of his possessions, very few, because he always traveled light.

I thought we would take the trip in two parts. We planned to stay one night with friends in San Francisco and leave the next day for Hawaii. As we walked through the airport to get our luggage, I asked my uncle numerous times if he was tired.

He'd always say, "Absolutely not." Perhaps he forgot he was tired; every moment was new to him. I didn't question his answer; I didn't know what his limits were, and we were new traveling companions.

When we got to San Francisco, he was so tired that he was disoriented. Uncle Sammy thought we were still in New York, and he wanted to walk home. I explained where we were, but he was convinced we were only a short distance from his apartment. He refused to go to my friend's home, and kept insisting we return to his. I was beside myself. Maybe this whole plan to relocate to Hawaii was a big mistake.

I had packed a tranquilizer in our luggage, never really believing I would need to use it. I pleaded with my uncle to take the pill since he was obviously tired and confused. He refused, for the first time not trusting me. He was still annoyed that I wouldn't just let him walk back to his apartment. He was rarely annoyed. I promised myself that we would return to his home if his upset continued. I thought, "I'll book the first flight back that I can, and be done with this plan."

I continued pleading, and he finally took the tranquilizer. We went to my friend's apartment. Sammy fell asleep in a big easy chair and slept for hours. I prayed while he slept. My prayer was, "Show me the way. If my uncle awakes and is still wanting to go home, then we will go back to New York immediately." I made return reservations, just in case.

Several hours later Sammy awoke. When he did, he looked around in amazement. He thought we were in the most glorious, sanctified of places. He touched everything he could, and couldn't stop marveling at the wonders. He was in a completely altered state of consciousness, somewhat ecstatic.

Uncle Sammy was also very hungry. We sat down to a meal. He was obviously still tired, because as we sat at the table, he began to butter his eyeglasses, still mesmerized by the profound beauty he saw all around him. My friends found Uncle delightful and hilarious. My prayer was answered.

The flight to Hawaii was uneventful, other than my uncle delighting the stewardesses with his wacky ways and obvious admiration of them. We arrived safely in Hawaii and went to my coffee shack home. I hoped it would be Uncle's new home, as well.

In Hawaii, Sammy was constantly enchanted, and he cast a spell of enchantment on those around him. He carried his magic with him, and that magic would be just as potent in the Islands as it was in New York.

CHAPTER 12

First Refrigerator Writing

As soon as we arrived in Hawaii I suggested to Sammy we begin the actual writing of our book. He quickly replied "Hell, yes!" with great enthusiasm. And so we began immediately on the refrigerator.

We were in the kitchen of our *coffee shack*, looking at the large white erase board we had installed on our fridge. After he stopped laughing, he instructed me to write his first quote. He said, "Write, 'I have only one thing on my mind ...'" He paused and said, suggestively, "Laughing." He then became quite serious, looking intently at the quote as it was written. Finally he said "No, two things: add, 'Kidding.'" He found this very funny. And so we began our very first session.

Our writing continued throughout the seven years we lived together. Uncle Sammy continued with his *wise wisecracks,* and I'd write them down some-time during the day. He loved editing them, and was very conscious of what he wished to convey. I'd write vignettes, little stories of our life together, and then read them to him. He was very engaged and reflec-tive at these times, the way a child becomes when she or he hears a fairy tale.

Sometimes Sammy seemed to behave in the style of certain Jewish comedians, comedians like George Burns. It was a vaudeville style, and they had emerged from the same archetype. At those times, he didn't crack a smile, even when everyone around him was laughing at his remarks. He was totally deadpan, although sometimes he managed to surprise himself with an unexpected remark. Then he would laugh with delight.

I said to him one day, "Uncle Sammy, what I love most about you is that I never know what will happen next." He replied, "That's what I love most about myself!"

Sammy's one-liners arose out of an awakened state. He was one with the present moment, a master of purposeful *schmoozing.* He resided in a joyful atmosphere, and he brought this atmosphere into our creative project.

CHAPTER 13

Unusually Incorporated

W hen my uncle came to live with me in Hawaii, we had to transfer his guardianship from New York to Hawaii, and I became his sole guardian. I soon found out that the legal guardianship aspects of his care were the most difficult.

There was only one judge who handled guardianships in our area. He was also the criminal court judge. Apparently, in his eyes, whoever appeared in his courtroom was guilty until proven innocent, even if no crime had been committed. This attitude was his method of crime prevention.

My uncle and I appeared in court together just once, and the judge asked my uncle only one question: "Mr. Green, how old are you?" Uncle Sammy replied, "Too old to remember." Just like in New York, the judge rolled his eyes, asked no more questions of

Uncle, and turned his attention to me. He asked me many questions in order to determine my fitness as Sammy's guardian. After this intense scrutiny we left the courtroom.

Uncle Sammy was jovial and quite talkative. He said some wonderful, wise things. He described himself as "unusually incorporated," and went on to say, "My system is not in that system. I can't help being perfect, but there's nothing like imperfection." Unfortunately, the judge heard none of it.

I felt this was a missed opportunity for the hearing to be uplifted. Sammy was seen as being so imperfect inside the courtroom. Yet, outside in the hallways, a whole different, delightful perfection was expressing itself. Several people, including a public defender, stopped to talk to my uncle simply because they found him so endearing. As he spoke, they were also delighted by his hilarious remarks.

Despite the fact that I was awarded the guardianship, and also because of that same fact, I was under suspicion for several years. The judge was constantly examining my actions and motives, almost looking for criminal behavior. At one point, early in the process, I appeared before the court with my annual accounting, and the judge said, "Ms. Siegel, I want you to understand that I'm not saying you committed a crime. I'm here to make sure you don't."

At one point I was aggrieved to hear the judge threaten to have my uncle placed in a care institution because his care at home was too expensive. I had to become a *peaceful warrior.* When I did research, I found the institutional costs to be exorbitant. Though I was upset, I knew I had to present this information calmly, as well as competently. I also knew that I would not allow Uncle Sammy to be removed from his home and my care, no matter what. He loved being at home, and we loved being with each other.

Eventually, numerous supportive letters from Uncle Sammy's doctor, the Day Center, and the community finally changed the judge's attitude toward me. We submitted articles about Elder care and dementia to him, along with our legal papers, and he began to learn more about this special area under his jurisdiction. It took almost five years, but at last I was no longer a *suspicious character.*

I made annual reports to the court to account for all spending. A court appointed Master was paid substantial fees to go over my records. They were always perfect because our dear friend, Jerry, was an incredible accountant. He was also very generous. He went over these records with diligence, and made sure they were in order.

It was uncanny how in tune Uncle Sammy and Jerry were. Uncle had appointed Jerry "Chairman of the Board" of our new company when he first met him. From the beginning, Sammy knew what I didn't know: that Jerry's depth of soul and intelligence would become essential for us. He was the only *official* with a serious job in our illustrious company. I remained the "guaranteed commander," in charge of my uncle's affairs.

WHO'S TAKING CARE OF WHO?

Beverly ... The Sacred and the Profane

After arriving in Hawaii with my uncle, I remembered that there was a woman named Beverly with a day care home for Elders, close to where we lived. I knew the woman's daughter, and had heard that her mother was a very caring and competent nurse.

Uncle Sammy and I went to *check it out.* The care home was located in a macadamia orchard, and as we walked toward the main building, he said to me, "Let's donate our happiness here." He often said this when he was feeling exceptionally jolly.

Sammy loved to meet new people and eagerly went to greet Beverly, who was approaching us. He took her hand in his, grinned at her, and said, "Why aren't you the God Ass?" She smiled and said, "You mean the Goddess!" "Hell, no!" he replied, "I mean the God Ass, spelled **G-O-D-A-S-S**." She looked a bit insulted and started to object. But he softened the moment, saying, "Don't worry about it. We're all in the same boat."

Once again, I saw him as a skillful spiritual teacher, a role I'd see him in time and time again. He was the *Wise Fool*. He would move you from compliment and inflation to insult and deflation, right through the paradox of not knowing. You would find yourself not being able to fit these interactions into any mental category and then wind up feeling silly and mirthful.

Beverly was a very good sport with a great sense of humor, and she took the *God Ass* introduction well, thinking that my uncle would liven things up. And he did.

He arrived the next day and met the other residents. They ate together. Since one or two of the people were disoriented, Beverly had a bulletin board viewable from the dining table. On that bulletin board was written the date, the day's activities, and which meal was next. The following day, Beverly had written, "The next meal is lunch," and someone else had mysteriously written, in much larger letters, "AND AFTER THAT NO MORE MEALS!" Beverly knew *that someone had to be Uncle Sammy,* though he would never admit it.

CHAPTER 14 • BEVERLY ... THE SACRED

Things got even livelier at the center. My uncle had his first liaison with an older woman named Florence. She was ninety, also a singer, and the two of them formed a duet. They sang show tunes at every opportunity. Unfortunately, Sammy's stay at this day care didn't last long. He was ousted. His flamboyant behavior and vigorous singing delighted the residents, but some of their visiting relatives were reserved, and wanted a more "respectable" atmosphere at the center. The new *duet* was simply too much for them.

My uncle had similar experiences within his own family. Our family was rather disturbed and embarrassed by my uncle's singing, anywhere, anytime, and this embarrassment extended to many of his other behaviors. It was for this reason that my uncle came to live happily with me in Hawaii, in an atmosphere where he could sing merrily anytime he wanted.

Beverly was sad about asking me to find another facility for Uncle, but he was the newest *kid* on the block, and the other residents had seniority. I was more than sad. We had to find another day care soon. I knew that caring for Uncle Sammy twenty-four hours a day was beyond my capacity, and that I needed assistance. Luckily, we soon found the Adult Day Center, another facility quite close to our home. Uncle Sammy would become a very popular person there, as well.

CHAPTER 15

Day Treatment Center Liberator

For a brief period after being ousted from Beverly's, I had been worried about finding a good caregiving situation: of course, Sammy wasn't. The Day Center fit the bill, a facility for disabled and older people who needed care during the day.

We checked it out. The staff was very kind. They had, as we say in Hawaii, great *aloha* spirit, and were upbeat people. Sammy and I both liked the programs. My uncle was enrolled.

At first, I was concerned because Sammy immediately got into trouble: it was his singing again. And not only was it his singing, but he was also yelling. The staff wrote him up. First it was "excessive singing" in his chart and I was consulted. Then it was "excessive singing and yelling," and I was asked to have Uncle Sammy re-evaluated by his doctor. When I asked Uncle about this behavior, he said, "I can't help myself. It feels so great. I want to yell like hell! I'm the greatest yeller in the world!" He was incorrigible.

The yelling was new, and when I investigated further, I found out that Uncle Sammy was yelling at a man who went into rages at the center. Uncle would intervene on behalf of the quieter patrons who couldn't handle these angry outbursts. It was a form of protectiveness. Fortunately, the man left the facility shortly thereafter, and Uncle stopped yelling. Unfortunately, Sammy also lost some of his vocal capacity, and could only sing softly. He did not have to go for the re-evaluation because he, and the situation, had shifted. After that storm subsided, I knew that the Day Center was our answer.

Everyone at the Day Center was assigned a locker with a piece of paper taped to the outside of it. Clients were asked to put their name on the paper. Uncle Sammy had great fun with this. He frequently changed his name on the locker door, at least for as long as he could write. As with everything else, Uncle became very playful with names and identity. Added to this playfulness was the fact that numerous mini-strokes had eliminated his ability to remember facts and details. On the locker he called himself "Sir George" or "George the Great." Another name he gave himself was "Mr. Hospitality," and then it was "Mr. Holiday," to which he added: "Just call me Mr. Holiday. My life is a holiday now," or "My life is pure poetry now! Just call me Nature Boy."

Sometimes he would also add other sayings onto the door of the locker:

"You can't be stopped from being great!"

"If you don't worry, you don't have to."

Uncle Sammy even had a self-assigned job there. Every day he stood at the door and spoke uplifting comments to the clients as they left for the day.

"Don't worry; I never do."

"It's all alright. Don't worry about a thing."

"You'll have everything you need."

"Go do beautiful things in a beautiful way."

He spoke these phrases with real caring and, of course, a humorous manner. Many of the patrons were scared and worried about aging or being disabled. They would smile back at Uncle Sammy, uplifted, reassured by him. He emanated a spirit of deep knowing. As I watched these interactions, I was so moved that, despite his increasing limitations, Sammy still had so much to give. It was his daily job. Difficult circumstances had not changed the spark of his consciousness. Inwardly liberated, he could offer loving kindness easily.

Both the staff and the other clients looked

forward to Sammy's caring gestures and humorous antics in an atmosphere where very little changed. Uncle Sammy's inventiveness and outrageousness interrupted routine at the Day Center. He brought a fun sense of aliveness wherever he went.

CHAPTER 16

On God

Uncle Sammy had a sort of daily schedule. He was always surprised and delighted when he saw the van from the Day Center pull up, happy to be going off in the morning, driven somewhere, by some "fella," never giving it a second thought.

Every time the van arrived, the drivers would get out in order to help Sammy, and the conversations would begin, conversations that I overheard each day. Uncle Sammy would greet the drivers with some quip pertinent to their lives. Since they were both religious, he would often talk to the two drivers about God. I had no inkling of their strong religious beliefs, yet Sammy knew.

He began many mornings with, "I talked to God today."

At once both drivers would answer, "And what did God say?"

Uncle would reply, "Didn't say anything. I did all the talking," or "God remembers. I can't."

Another morning they might ask, "Did you speak to God today?"

He would reply, "I'm speaking to God all the time."

They were always very interested in the daily God conversations, as was I, never knowing what Uncle would come up with.

"Do you know where God is?" He would point to his own heart and say, "He's right in here. God likes what I do, so I don't ask for answers. I don't want to smother him with too many questions. I want him to feel free."

On another occasion he began again with, "I actually spoke to God."

When they said, "What did he say?" he said, "You should know that; you're God."

They laughed so hard, even though I suspected that they never kidded about God in this manner except with Uncle. He was so innocent, so empty of any insult or malice that they never took offense.

All the while Sammy remained the *trickster*. When the drivers came expecting something funny, Uncle would become deep and philosophical. If they came expecting a talk, he would, instead, start singing opera at the top of his lungs.

To one of the men, who was extremely humble and almost self-effacing, he said, "God told me you are one of the most amazing fellas on this planet, so down to earth and caring." And he was.

Sammy didn't only engage the drivers with his God talk. I overheard him say to an *Elderly*, very disabled lady at the Day Center, "Pardon me lady, but are you God?" She was so flabbergasted that she burst out laughing.

Uncle Sammy never was religious in an orthodox sense, but he always maintained a *Crazy Wisdom spirituality*. He never spoke about God or religion until his dementia freed him from more earthly, practical concerns, and then he spoke about God often. He became a pastor of sorts. Many of his comments used humor as the vehicle, and those comments focused on the divinity within people.

Some might mistake what he did. But to me he was the *Irreverent Reverend*.

CHAPTER 17

WHAT THE HELL!

Respect was very important to Sammy. My uncle definitely did not take kindly to anyone presuming to know better than he did what he *should* be doing. His usual sunny, funny personality always noticed when someone was patronizing or demeaning to him. He would cut off this intrusion quickly and effectively with humor or direct anger.

When anyone in our family was looking to blame anyone else, Uncle Sammy would take the role of the blameworthy: exaggerate the offense, playfully, and take the blame. I remember an incident from my childhood when my cousin Ronald was driving. We were suddenly lost, and the rest of the family was getting upset with Ronald. Sammy acted as if he had led my cousin astray. The mood was broken, and I was so relieved.

After he was officially diagnosed with dementia,

my uncle was often the target for condescension and control, and he used his "WHAT THE HELL!" technique to combat those attitudes. Family members and caregivers in New York did not understand his unique gifts and delightful ways of being. I saw relatives embarrassed by Sammy, trying to shush him and stop him when he was singing. I saw caregivers attempt to handle his affairs without sufficient respect. On these occasions, he showed righteous anger and frustration in order to offset this treatment. He was quite effective. Whenever anyone tried to override him or stop him from doing what he wanted to do, he'd vociferously yell, "WHAT THE HELL!" as many times as was needed, then return to his usual jovial demeanor.

Soon after Uncle had moved to Hawaii, I hired an experienced caregiver to assist me. He had all kinds of ideas about activities he and Uncle Sammy *should* engage in. He felt he knew better than Sammy what Sammy *ought to do*. Uncle let the man know, in no uncertain terms, that he had to go … a few "WHAT THE HELLS" did it. I never had to intervene. Sammy knew what assistance he needed and didn't need.

Though respect and autonomy remained core issues for my uncle, he could easily let go of his anger. One morning, I was distracted and washing his face too quickly, perhaps roughly. He momentarily became angry and yelled his usual "WHAT THE HELL!" with that surprisingly powerful and forceful energy in his voice. A moment later, when I had completed the task more gently, I said, "Sorry." He looked at me, completely puzzled, and said, "My dear child, let's sing." His response was so fresh and immediate. He had completely forgotten what had just transpired, and was already encountering the next moment with new possibilities.

When he felt disrespected, he acted immediately to remove that disrespect. In telling someone to *back off,* Uncle Sammy was free from negativity. His emotions were currents moving through him, not stagnant pools. He didn't deplete his energy with habitual responses. As he took action, there was no reactivity or defensiveness; therefore his actions were powerful. He was an amazing example of the right use of anger and pure energy. He let it out, he let it go, and he moved into the next moment with exactly what was needed.

Given respect and treated with dignity, my uncle returned easily to the realm of spirit and its powerful source. And once there, other aspects of his being were revealed and flourished. He then engaged fully with others, soul to soul, enchanted by them and the present moment. He entered a field of play, treating laughter as sacred territory, and invited others to join.

CHAPTER 18

On Laughter

"I have no time not to fool around." For Uncle Sammy, laughter was a form of worship. Every morning when I greeted my uncle, he'd insist we practice laughing meditation together. He would begin by looking at me with the eyes of a true sage and the innocence of a young child. I felt like he could connect to my very essence. Uncle Sammy would say, "There you are, my dear child," and laugh. He might give some spontaneous comment:

"I live life up, not down!"

"I want you to be a person who laughs a lot!"

"I practice laughing night and day!"

"I have a great responsibility to have fun!"

Then he would always break into laughter, and keep laughing and laughing. Sometimes, when I didn't feel like joining in, he'd pause momentarily and gaze at me with that knowing look. Then he'd start up again until I was just caught up in laughter with him.

At home we laughed everyday at his *tips and quips*. He turned so many beliefs and notions completely upside down.

"I'm busy being busy," he would say. And he often apologized like this:

"I apologize for being perfect. There's nothing like imperfection!"

He addressed so many mental traps with his humor.

Uncle Sammy remained vibrantly alive in a body which increasingly lost function. And his aliveness showed up in unexpected moments.

Some days at the Day Center there would be a somber atmosphere, especially if one of the clients had just died. I walked in one day to pick up my uncle. He had been pretty quiet for a substantial period of time, the residual effects of a few mini-strokes. When I arrived, he was at the far end of the room. As Sammy saw me, he yelled, with great strength in his voice:

"There she is! She's come to take me home and tie me up."

It was so unexpected. He hadn't said a full sentence in a long time and the content ... I walked over to his side. Everyone was laughing at this absurdity. I asked, "So what will I do with you after I've tied you up?" He quickly replied, "You know what you'll do with me," still in that pseudo-sexual mode.

He was a master of surprise. Everyone lightened up, thrown off guard by his humor.

We had a lovely, very serious guest from the mainland. Ingrid is a fabric designer and painter. She had come to Hawaii on a search to rekindle her creativity and to recover from the dissolution of a relationship.

At this point, Uncle Sammy spoke very little, and he didn't seem to notice her at all. Ingrid was in her own world, and didn't relate to *him* at all. Suddenly, one morning, she asked to meet my uncle. She appeared in front of him. He said "Hello," looked at her, started to laugh, and kept laughing. At first she was startled. Her rational mind didn't know what was going on. Then she got it, and tried to laugh along with him. Forcing it at first, it became more and more natural until she started to laugh, uncontrollably. She laughed and laughed and laughed some more. She completely got my uncle's intention. It was the first time in her ten-day visit that she was not serious.

She left the very next day, and soon we received two e-mails from her.

The first e-mail said: "When I arrived home I wanted to see the sunrise at Mount Diablo. I drove there and camped overnight. I woke very early the next morning with this strong, tangible sensation of a laugh slowly rising like a big, warm bubble in my stomach and then coming out of my mouth. It was Uncle Sammy's laugh. That sound was only in my dream, though, so when I was fully awake I had to practice it. Then I went further up the mountain and chanted to the four directions. I also painted that afternoon. Thank you, and give Uncle Sammy a big hug and big thanks."

The second e-mail arrived some weeks later. In it she said:

"I have a new sweetie who has the greatest sense of humor and laugh and it's infectious. HA HA HA."

The e-mails reinforced my understanding that Uncle carried strong, positive medicine for people. He knew just what each person needed in order to shift his or her usual perspective.

I told Uncle Sammy, and he just nodded with a radiant grin.

He was truly a *wise guy*.

Sammy focused on honoring *divine foolishness*, holding laughter in a pinnacle position, knowing it to be central to sacred experience. When I saw a photo of "Sufi Sam" with his laughing hat, I recognized that Uncle Sammy had the same archetypal energy. Sufi Sam, Samuel Lewis Ahmed Murad Chisti, was a Sufi Master. My uncle was also a messenger of this archetype, and his expression of it became more and more refined throughout his dementia. He was radiantly conscious of this job.

Sammy wore special hats. He began to wear sailor hats, and with his new mustache, he looked a bit like Popeye. A few trips through the washing machine and the hats shape-shifted; they became *yarmulkes,* akin to a type of hat worn by many different Middle Eastern and Indian spiritual folks. They seemed perfect to do his *healing* work. When anyone looked at him in these hats, they would invariably smile, as his image called forth many other images, timeless and universal.

As Uncle used fewer words, he lived more and more in a sea of laughter, below the level of words. He played in an energy field with sound, movement, gestures, and facial expressions, an atmosphere of possibility and openness. This unorthodox sage-trickster used his humor and his mastery of the unexpected to cross boundaries, to jump the track of ordinary consciousness, and reach a world not governed by ordinary rules.

CHAPTER 19

The Big Checks

My uncle was one of the most cheerful people I knew, and it took very little to increase his rapture. He had some unusual means of keeping himself in good spirits.

When I began taking care of his practical matters, I noticed he had written various notes to himself and put them in his wallet. They read, "S.G.G. (his initials) gets $1,500,000.00," or "S.G.G. gets $2,000,000.00." These notes would make him sing loudly and put a big smile on his face.

Over time he started losing things, including his wallet and his ability to write, so no more notes. I decided to remedy the situation by writing him checks for huge sums of money. I would leave them around the house where he could easily find them. The checks made Sammy ecstatically happy for days. He loved feeling rich, and he had very generous ideas about how to spend these huge sums.

For a long time this game worked, until one night, when Sammy woke me up at 3 a.m., so excited to have found a million dollar check during his night time roaming. He wanted to buy a brand new convertible for Francis, his sweetheart who lived in New York and had never driven. He was incredulous at my apparent indifference. How could I be so blasé and refuse to accompany him to the bank at 3 a.m.? With great difficulty, I persuaded him to go back to bed.

These nocturnal visits began to happen on a regular basis. Reason seemed out of the question, as this check-writing scheme of mine was outside the realm of reason. We usually interfaced our realities quite easily, though not on these sleepless nights.

I stopped writing the checks.

I needed sleep.

CHAPTER 20

On the Run Again

My uncle developed a new love once he moved to Hawaii: hula. I took him to see some hula dance shows, and in a short time he began to combine hula moves with opera riffs. He easily picked up swaying his torso, Hawaiian-style, and started speaking Hawaiian *pidgin,* and saying, "How's it?" instead of, "Yo," his slang expression from the New York streets.

Our neighbors didn't see the hula moves, but they heard the singing and thought Sammy was a retired opera singer. That reputation got around the entire neighborhood. Uncle would usually just smile when people asked him. Or when he did speak, was so good at *wise* wise cracks that initially people did not realize he had no idea of temporal reality.

When I heard about a show in Waimea with some of the top Hawaiian groups, I knew we had to go. My friends Jerry and Mica were eager to come along. They always enjoyed outings with Uncle, never knowing exactly what kind of experience it would be.

We drove up to Waimea, a town in the mountains about an hour away, and stopped at an ice cream shop across the parking lot from the theatre. Uncle Sammy was pleased. Ice cream was still his favorite food.

After the first group's performance, Uncle had to go to the bathroom. I took him to the men's room and waited outside. I waited and waited: no Uncle. Finally my friend Jerry walked by, looking for us. I asked him to go into the bathroom and get Uncle Sammy. He came back out a few seconds later and reported that there was no one in the men's bathroom. "That's impossible," I said. "I've been standing here waiting for him the whole time." He repeated, "No one's in there." I decided to look for myself. I opened the door to the men's bathroom and saw two inner doors: one led into the men's toilets and the other had "Stage Door" written on it. It led backstage.

I grabbed Jerry and we both walked backstage. There were several large groups of Hawaiian performers. We asked the first group "Did you see a tiny, *Elderly* man wearing a trench coat pass by?" They said, "Yes," and pointed further on. We kept going, group after group, until we went past all the groups and found another stage door that went outside. We went out and looked, but no sign of him. I went to get my other friend to help us look and let her know what had happened. We looked everywhere. At this point I was starting to panic. Where on earth could he be? We'd searched everywhere! We searched some more.

Just before I was about to call the police, I saw Uncle Sammy with a policeman, strolling across the parking lot towards the theatre. He was beaming at the policeman as they chatted. Uncle Sammy had a gigantic ice cream cone in one hand, and was holding the policeman's hand in the other. He was completely happy, unconcerned, and eating his favorite treat, which the officer had been charmed into buying for him.

Somehow, magically, it had all worked out, and once again he was protected.

THE UNION OF BEAUTIFUL WOMEN

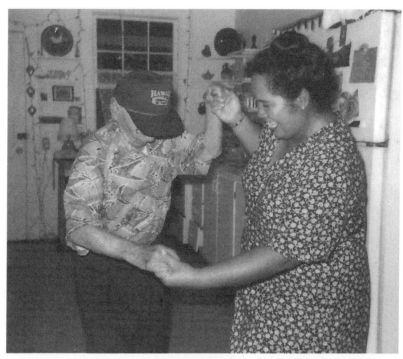

CHAPTER 21

Sammy and the Union of Beautiful Women

Grace was the first of my uncle's private caregivers, and a primary member of what Sammy came to call his *Union of Beautiful Women.*

Grace is a Hawaiian woman, strong, able-bodied, with bountiful long thick black hair. She felt that caregiving was her true calling from *Spirit*; a spiritual assignment. When one sees her with *her people,* one cannot help but recognize this. She is also naturally gracious and respectful to all people. There is a deep spirit of *aloha* within her.

Grace and Uncle shared so much affection. They were both such *lovers.* Sammy kept respectfully telling Grace that she was a most beautiful creature, and indeed she is. Uncle would say to Grace, "Your heart is just the way it should be." Sammy also called her *the boss* or *the coach*. He was always instinctually elevating people to their true status.

One day, as Sammy was kidding with her and lauding her great qualities, Grace broke down in tears of gratitude. She said, "Uncle always knows when I'm having a hard week." He somehow knew when she was not being appreciated. She lit up when Uncle Sammy would say to me, deliberately within her earshot, "Oh Grace ... she is the most *gorgeous* creature." With his so-called dementia and *being out there,* Uncle Sammy was really so *in there* and in touch.

When she had her caregiving shift in the afternoon, Grace would take Uncle to her home. He enjoyed going almost anywhere, especially with Grace. Sammy would be there when her husband returned from work. Uncle felt her husband didn't appreciate her enough, and he would let him know in ways no one would tolerate, except from a *holy fool.*

As Grace's husband came in the door, Sammy would be sitting in Mr. X's favorite chair. As soon as Uncle saw him, he would yell, "And who are you?!" At dinner my uncle would freely partake of those dishes prepared especially for Mr. X, sometimes eating the whole thing, indicating he considered Mr. X unworthy of such special treatment. In front of her husband, Uncle would often say to Grace, "You are such a gorgeous creature." All of these antics helped both Grace and her husband realize her true worth.

One day as Sammy again referred to Grace as a gorgeous being I asked, "Uncle Sammy, are you in love with Grace?" He replied, "No." Then I asked if I was a gorgeous being, too, kidding but also hoping for an affirmative answer. He paused and said, "Nooo …" My heart was a little disappointed. *Was Grace the only gorgeous creature in his eyes?* Then he went on, "Just gorgeous. We are all simply gorgeous." He got me again.

Uncle Sammy had an amazing sense of comedic timing that left gaps for both the truth and the unexpected to show up. With his *fool's ways* he healed.

CHAPTER 22

Heidi's Breakthrough

Heidi, a vivacious German woman who sometimes helped care for Uncle Sammy, liked to come over and visit us, even on her days off. She appeared one day and said to Uncle, "I just had to see you. I'm feeling frustrated and so creatively blocked."

As she leaned over to kiss Sammy, he suddenly shouted, "Breakthrough!"

Heidi started laughing, looking quite amazed, and said, "That's exactly what I've been praying for these last few days: a *breakthrough*."

Uncle Sammy was so sudden and forceful in his response that she left shortly afterward, quite convinced of the certainty of a breakthrough. A few days later, she returned to bring Uncle the gift of a painting. Since her big moment with him, she had been painting furiously. She definitely had a creative breakthrough.

Heidi said she was so fond of Uncle Sammy for many reasons. Her own dad was a very cold authoritarian who undermined her. Heidi is multitalented, and could not remember her father encouraging her about anything. She is a musician and an artist. She would come over and play her accordion and sing German folk songs for Uncle Sammy. He was so appreciative, accompanying her with his *made up* songs and frequently exclaiming, "Wonderful! Beautiful!"

Heidi was delighted by Uncle's capacity to be such a positive father figure when he was so incapacitated in other ways. Sammy was the first nurturing, masculine influence in her life. He was a person who opened her up to so many magical, mystical possibilities.

CHAPTER 23

Emily and the Sacred Fun Tradition

(Re-funning the World)

Emily and Uncle were dear friends. It was wonderful to see them together. She had the beautiful vitality of a youthful being, and he had the beautiful vitality of an ageless *rascal sage*. They *hit it off* as soon as they met, and she, too, became a caregiver for him. Emily was definitely in the *Union of Beautiful Women*.

She later told me, "I was in my early twenties when I met Uncle Sammy, and it was a marvel to meet someone who was a mystic, who had an alternative reality from most people. His was a playful reality, and yet so wise. When he sent out his energy to engage another person, he somehow knew how this person needed to be met. It was almost a sonar pulse of light energy, sent out to play. He showed me human possibilities.

"When I first met him, he was in a hospital bed, and he was very quiet. Since I had worked in convalescent homes earlier, I came with certain expectations, and I had no idea *who* was in that bed. But soon I learned who he was: an amazing Elder, full of surprises, mystic sayings, and sagely advice.

"At the time I was in a difficult life situation. I had just recently gotten married, and our marriage wasn't going well. After a short while, my husband was pressuring me to get a better paying job. I refused. I told him that Uncle Sammy got me laughing every day. Where would I find another job with that fringe benefit? I insisted on staying."

One afternoon, Emily was talking with me about her marriage. She was confused, and she was trying to decide whether to stay or leave. Uncle Sammy was sitting on the other side of the table, appar-ently *paying us no mind*. He was not talking much that day. All of a sudden he shouted, "Going, going, gone!"

We burst out laughing. It was the truth. Emily knew she had to leave, but she hadn't yet admitted it to herself.

On another occasion she came to work, very upset, but hadn't said a word about it. Uncle Sammy dropped what he was engaged in and said, "What can I do to help you?"

"It was so real, so genuine, caring, and straight from his heart." Emily was touched. Here was Uncle with many physical limitations, yet able to deeply give to her.

She said, "Sammy really paid attention to other people, and seemed to know what they essentially needed to heal. He taught everyone how to care for him by embodying the Golden Rule. He helped others thrive with levity and appropriate medicine. He told me, 'Trust the way things are,' and 'Go beyond the beyond.' "

"He was such a good companion—always light enough to play. He would say to me, 'I'm ready for anything!' and he was."

Uncle Sammy and I would go on outings in the neighborhood, and we thoroughly enjoyed ourselves. On these outings, Uncle's sayings came spontaneously, and they delivered a big wallop because of the surprise factor! After a while, they really seemed to come *out of the blue,* as Uncle had lost so much of his capacity for speech because of mini-strokes.

He said suddenly one day, "Life is a heaven of dreams. Fix it up and keep it going."

"If you don't worry, you don't have to."

"I have a big responsibility to have fun."

He really did honor that responsibility. Emily stayed with Uncle Sammy until he died.

"I still can hear his laugh, and I find myself laughing just like Uncle Sammy: 'heh, heh, heh, heh.' He added joy and lightness to my life."

After Sammy died, I saw Emily at her new job. She told me Uncle had come to her in the dreamtime. He suggested to her that they "re-fun" the world and form a "Sacred Fun Tradition." From her description, it sounded like my uncle was still on the job, and that he was enlisting help from his buddies who hadn't crossed over yet.

CHAPTER 24

Malia and Uncle Sammy

Malia was in the Union of Beautiful Women. Sammy really liked her; she was gentle and respectful, with a hearty, infectious laugh. She found Uncle Sammy delightfully funny and wise, and I can remember so clearly hearing them laugh together a lot.

This is how she reminisced about him:

"In the beginning I was overly careful, even fussy, about *doing everything right*. I wanted to consult him on every detail. When I was too meticulous or solicitous, or trying too hard to be good, he'd either say, 'Yeah, yeah,' paying me no mind, or yell, 'WHAT THE HELL!' suddenly. As soon as I stopped, he'd stop, and he would laugh and joke with me. He set me straight pretty quick, and I would laugh and relax and see the bigger picture. He didn't hold onto anything for long. He was so present and wanted me to be present, to be myself, not nervously doing things. That was one of my greatest lessons.

"He could let you know a truth in perfect timing. Because there was no ego involved, I could accept it. He came from such a pure source, mostly spirit, pure joy, pure anger, and not from a defended self-image or personality, as so many of us do. He didn't want anything back: no accolades, no agenda. It was uncalculated, a truth revealed with perfect timing. He was lucid in a way that was powerful and unexpected. On some level, he really knew what needed to be said or done.

"When he'd get up at night, I'd worry about him getting enough sleep and try to get him back to bed. He would just be fascinated with everything ... his bedroom, the light in his bedroom, the light in the fridge. He really loved and was fascinated by light. He would open the fridge and say, each time, 'Oh what a beautiful light.' He would look at his room each time with fresh new vision, and say, 'Look at that beautiful ...,' whatever it was. To him everything was fresh, new, and beautiful. I also learned that from him.

"My grandmother was dying not long after I met Uncle Sammy, and I felt I could be with her, be present in a new way. I went to visit her, and stayed in the hospital with her, and it was very beautiful. Sammy and I used to sing together, so I found myself able to sing hymns with my grandmother, and it was very touching for both of us.

"Several years later I lost my mother, father, and sister within a short time of each other. I learned so much about being with them, *really* being with them, in the time we had left, from my experience with Uncle Sammy.

"I remember meeting a friend at a coffee shop, long after I had cared for Uncle. I really liked this person, but he would go on and on in a disorganized, cerebral way. He was so mental. Usually I would try very hard to understand him, and wind up very frustrated. This time I noticed that I wasn't trying so hard, and when he finished, I said, 'Yeah, yeah, yeah, gotta go.' I walked away laughing to myself. It felt as if a wave of energy came over me, as if Uncle Sammy's spirit had washed over me, and his words just came out of my mouth, and I felt so free."

Malia placed a picture of Uncle Sammy on her altar as one of her finest teachers.

CHAPTER 25

Enjoy the Ride

It was my Uncle Sammy's eighty-fourth birthday. He had on his checkered blazer, the only remaining piece of clothing from his New York days, and a baseball cap that read "Hang Loose," the only other piece of Hawaii in his attire beside his *aloha* shirt. He was also sporting a new mustache, which he loved to fondle. He was, as always, willing to go anywhere and try anything. So out we went with an assemblage of friends who were extremely fond of my uncle and his ways.

At previous birthday celebrations Sammy had made speeches, and that night there was an air of expectancy about what kind of speech he might come up with. We went to a restaurant, and before ordering our meals, Uncle unwrapped his birthday presents. The one he was most taken with was a magazine entitled *Cars and Motorcycles*. He kept going through the pages, while he was eating, entirely absorbed, sometimes forgetting which plate was his and dipping into the plates on either side of him (perhaps not forgetting). He often assumed that everything around him was available, and not necessarily for the *normal* uses.

I had my notebook ready, prepared to jot down whatever new quotes might go in our book. All of a sudden Uncle Sammy lifted his head from the *Cars and Motorcycles* magazine, looked at our friend George, and said, with great enthusiasm:

"Enjoy the Ride!"

It took a few moments, but then George got the message, and he started repeating the phrase along with Uncle Sammy.

"Enjoy the Ride!"

"Enjoy the Ride!"

Once George got it, Uncle went on to Jerry, who was looking puzzled. Sammy kept looking at him until finally Jerry caught on.

"Enjoy the Ride!"

Our friend Jay was already along for the ride. Uncle Sammy's penetrating glance caught up with Kathleen, who didn't understand, until his light-hearted persistence finally had her laughing uncontrollably.

At this point, we all got it, this teaching on

enjoying life, this ride. Uncle Sammy, who was in a wheelchair, with a bit of paralysis on one side, unconcerned about who he was or where he was, was completely *Enjoying the Ride.*

CHAPTER 26

Tuning into K-JOY

After the *Enjoy the Ride* birthday celebration, I was speaking with Kathleen, who had been at the party. She said, "Every time I see Uncle Sammy, I notice he's not on the channel or station I'm on. I've always thought our brains are like radio or TV receivers, and Uncle Sammy is definitely tuned into K-JOY, not K-FEAR. I wish I could get there as easily."

I remembered looking at an old photo of my uncle when he was in his twenties, and he had written on the back of the photo, "The Happy Warrior, a study in arrogance, insolence, and the sickening grin." In the photo he had a huge grin, and I realized that he delighted in laughing at himself. Joyful lightness was never far from his consciousness.

In later years, one of his nicknames for himself was Mr. Feelgood.

Until the day he died, I never ceased to be amazed by the fact that my uncle constantly stayed tuned into K-JOY.

CHAPTER 27

Sammy's Eighty-Fifth with the Union of Beautiful Women

"Have fun. You'll be better off."
My friend Nancy was another of Uncle Sammy's Union of Beautiful Women. She liked to kiss and pinch his cheeks and do a good bit of *kibitzing around*. She dearly loved her own father, but he was afraid of aging, which saddened her. So Uncle Sammy was a wonderful surrogate father to her.

At his first birthday dinner in Hawaii, Nancy had witnessed how Uncle Sammy had suddenly started eating voraciously after months of eating very little. She knew that, previously, his housekeepers in New York had seen him as a senile old man about to die. He had gradually begun eating less and less, until he had almost stopped eating completely. His will to live, along with his appetite, had diminished.

There were two men and a good many women at that birthday celebration, Sammy's eightieth. Uncle became rambunctious after seeing how people valued him and were there to honor him. First, he stood up and made a hilarious speech. Then, he not only finished his own dinner but also ate so much of the dinners of the people on either side of him that we had to order more food. He ate heartily after the party, and my worry, in that regard, was over. It really touched me deeply to see that love and respect from others could move Sammy so swiftly into joy and commitment to his own life. He then passed that joy and commitment on to others. After that significant time, he showed amazing dignity toward himself, and he maintained that dignity, even in the most physically trying times at the end of his life.

Five years later, on his eighty-fifth birthday, Nancy insisted on helping organize the celebration. She even arranged to begin the festivities in a bright red 1954 Buick convertible.

The plan was to take him out with six women from his Union of Beautiful Women for a drive in this convertible, very red and very sassy. Then we would take him out to dinner at his favorite restaurant. When we arrived at the Day Center to start our date, Uncle Sammy was tired and a bit grumpy. I found it unusual that he left without saying, "Don't worry. I never do," to the other folks attending that day. I was quite concerned at the beginning of the drive, because he hadn't even noticed this elegant vehicle. Uncle had owned a similar vehicle as a young man. Often he would see an early model car and offer some quip, inspired by that vision. Not this time.

Sammy, the Union, and the Red Buick

Once again ice cream came to the rescue. As soon as we possibly could, we bought him a Neapolitan ice cream sandwich. It worked. With the first few bites of his ice cream sandwich, he became gay and effusive. We were now on purpose, and our drive to the restaurant was ceremonious and poignant. As we went to pick up all the other celebrants, Uncle Sammy got out of the car and greeted each woman with clear, open presence and sweet talk. All of the women were decked out for the occasion in their glamorous best. Uncle looked each woman up and down, fully appreciating her outer form as well as her inner beauty. He was also decked out in his Hawaiian cap with the *shaka* on it, a Hawaiian hand signal indicating "How's it?"

At the small, local restaurant he had six women rolling in laughter throughout the dinner. Several men called out to him and asked what his special *technique* was. He went to each of their tables, *kibitzed* with them, sang a bit, and then came back to the Union. He stood up and made several speeches, saying, for example, "Trust the way things are. It's the only way to be," or "I say we should be just where we are." Other patrons heard him singing at the top of his lungs, and someone asked him if he was a retired opera singer.

As he said at his birthday party,

"My life will be pure poetry from now on. We're all coming together. Bless the day."

CHAPTER 28

Reggie's B&B

It was never hard to find caregivers for Uncle Sammy once his reputation for fun got around. On some occasions, when I went out of town, Uncle stayed at a local bed-and-breakfast. Reggie was the owner, and she sometimes did caregiving for Elders. Uncle was her favorite.

She and her family were so fond of Sammy that each time I would come to pick him up, they'd say; "Sammy can stay with us anytime. He keeps us laughing. He is soooo entertaining!" They enjoyed sitting together with him, relaxing on their *lanai,* the Hawaiian word for deck. Reggie didn't like to move around much and neither did her large, Hawaiian husband. They loved to eat and laugh, as did Uncle Sammy. It was a perfect match for everyone concerned.

On one occasion, I returned from a trip and went

to pick him up. Reggie couldn't stop laughing. She said, "Whenever we think he's not paying attention, he comes out with something, seemingly out of nowhere, a *non sequitur* that doesn't make any sense at first, and then makes a lot of sense if you look at it differently. He really makes us think. We began to kid him:

"Who sent you anyway? Are you some kind of spy?"

Uncle also had a lot of fun with Reggie's guests. I didn't know how much fun until much later. I became friends with a woman who lived in Hawaii, and, by chance, had met my uncle when she first arrived. In one of our conversations I mentioned Sammy, and she recognized him, and related this story:

Her first journey to Hawaii was on her honeymoon. She was staying at Reggie's B&B. She and her husband had arrived at Reggie's late at night. They planned to sleep in as they were feeling pretty exhausted from all of their wedding festivities.

Early the next morning, there was an insistent knock at the door. Reluctantly, she went to answer. Standing there was this tiny man, wearing just a trench coat, who began to sing opera to them. He beamed at her with happy innocence. This outlandish occurrence sent her into gales of laughter, and she invited him in. He provided just the comic relief they needed. He was their unlikely hero who gave their marriage a good start and a little magic.

This story was not unusual. Numerous times I would hear tales about Sammy's spontaneous interactions with people after the fact.

Although he had limited mobility, my uncle really seemed to get around.

CHAPTER 29

Georging It Up

The Union of
Beautiful Women and George

We were at the Aloha Café. My uncle was kidding around with our favorite waitress, Donna, when in walked George, an acquaintance who would later become a very close family friend.

The first thing Uncle Sammy said to him was, "Hello. Why, you're a megalomaniac."

George does, in fact, have a big head, but it's a big head of curly hair. That wasn't exactly what Uncle Sammy meant. Sammy looked so frail and innocent, and his remark startled George. Meeting this person who was moving so very slowly on one level, yet so quickly on another, was enough to throw George off guard and into a state of deep introspection.

George took several days to look up the meaning

of *megalomaniac* and try to figure out its significance. Once he realized that *megalomaniac* meant *bigheaded*, he was able to stop taking himself so seriously. Uncle captivated George's interest: he made a potentially offensive remark without causing offense. George was able to look within and get another glimpse of himself. Once again, Sammy helped someone to quickly see where they were caught in an illusion, and then kindly spin them out of it with humor.

After they became better acquainted, Uncle Sammy invited George to "George it up" with him (Uncle Sammy's middle name was George), and they did. George is an arborist and very dedicated to plants. He has felt great sadness about human destruction to our earth's ecology. Uncle understood his dilemma. He liked George very much, and was always trying to get him to laugh and lighten up, quite effectively. It seemed that Uncle Sammy brought out a humorous and tender side of George, and he helped George enjoy what a funny life it is. That's what he'd meant by "Georging it up." After all, if someone with all of Uncle's disabilities could lighten up, why couldn't he? More and more often I would often catch George smiling or laughing as he sat with Uncle. He became one of Uncle Sammy's best pals and caregivers.

After Uncle broke his hip and went to a facility for rehabilitation, George would take Sammy to a spot on the facility's grounds where they could sit in silence and see and smell the ocean. Whenever I saw them there, they both exuded a sense of deep peace. I was certain this companionship of another man assisted Uncle to feel the larger vista of his existence.

The day that Sammy was discharged, it was hilarious to watch as George assisted him into his car, to his *liberation* from the facility. To Uncle Sammy, both our dog, Chico, and George were *Noble Fellows*. George was the only man in the union of caregivers for Uncle Sammy, and we agreed to rename it "The Union of Beautiful Women and George."

After Uncle died, many people who knew him had *visits*. George was very moved by a visit from my uncle shortly after he passed away. Sammy appeared as a strong presence in a dream. He thanked George for his love and companionship in such a touching way that George woke up crying. He hadn't cried in a long, long time. His heart opened. He said he felt himself more ready to both give and receive love. Uncle Sammy, that happy warrior of the heart, had blessed him.

Being of service to Uncle Sammy was so gratifying to George that, to this day, he feels service is his new, true purpose.

The secret of ice cream

CHAPTER 30

Ice Cream Checks

Jay and Her Ice Cream Truck

After I had to stop writing the checks for millions to my uncle, Jay, another member of Sammy's "Union of Beautiful Women," began to write him ice cream checks.

Along with caring for uncle on occasions, Jay drove an ice cream truck. She lived in the big house just up the road from us, and would drive right by our house on her way to work. She always sounded her special jingle to let us know the ice cream truck was on its way to us.

At the time, we were living in what was called, in our area, a *coffee shack:* a tiny cottage in a coffee-growing area. Usually Uncle and I would be sitting outside on the small porch as the truck approached. Uncle Sammy could not believe his luck each and every time the ice cream truck would stop at our house. Uncle believed ice cream was one of the secrets of life, if not the major secret, in competition with laughter. Jay, a longtime friend, who didn't eat ice cream herself, agreed with Uncle Sammy about the power of its magic.

Jay would jingle, stop the truck, and show Uncle all the different ice creams. Each time it would be as if it was for the first time, and for him, each time was totally fresh. After handing him an ice cream, she would give him a handwritten check for several more ice creams. He loved this, and would reread the check several times each time it was given, and many more times before he received the next one, in absolute, pure delight.

Jay had gotten this check idea after she found out that Uncle Sammy's million dollar checks had to stop. Uncle Sammy was equally pleased with these checks.

CHAPTER 31

Uncle Sammy, the Cosmic Jester

Our neighbor and friend Pati told me this story about meeting Uncle Sammy for the first time: "My friend, Emily, brought Sammy along to a world peace meditation that we were attending. We all stood in a circle, holding hands with our eyes closed. Emily was directly across from me, and Sammy was right next to her, sitting comfortably in his wheelchair. We focused on world healing, toning to the sounds of 'ahs' and 'oms.' I found myself being guided through my *chakras*, seeing and feeling a healing vision for each one. The sixth *chakra* in the middle of my forehead was particularly painful, and I began to cry. The pain subsided, and my attention was drawn to the crown of my head and then several feet above. There I saw a vision of Uncle Sammy! He was pointing down at all of us and laughing. I peeked out of one eye to find the actual Uncle Sammy in an uproarious giggle. Quickly closing my eyes again, my tears were transformed into a glorious, relieving laughter. It was all so funny: the serious effort we all were making in the play of our lives, while believing in the solid reality of our world stage.

"Uncle Sammy really got the cosmic joke, and so did I."

CHAPTER 32

Aloha and the Kiss

In Hawaii, as in New York, my uncle and I enjoyed going for walks. In the town of Kealakekua there were several banks we frequented. Banks were still one of Sammy's favorite institutions. The women tellers were always happy to see my uncle and hear him sing. He definitely was not their routine customer. Since he had a very strong belief that we are all beautiful creatures, he would *dutifully* let each woman know that she was beautiful, either by saying this directly, or by singing a little made-up ditty. If I came in without him, they'd always ask for him, and insist I bring him the next time. But Sammy didn't limit his charm to bank tellers.

In the next town, Kainaliu, we'd go to our favorite restaurant, The Aloha Café, next to which was the Aloha Gift Store. Sammy was Mr. Aloha himself. He knew all the clerks, and they knew him. He also knew some of the regular customers. They were part of our neighborhood *gang*. No one guessed that he had been diagnosed with dementia, as his *kibitzing* was so quick and clever. He had some great chats in that store.

One afternoon, we were visiting the store and Cindy, one of the regular customers, was there. She was not her usual, perky self, but offered Uncle Sammy her usual kiss. Sammy pretended to swoon and in a very dramatic voice said, "That was the kiss of a lifetime! In all my years, *never* have I experienced a kiss like that kiss." We all laughed at his theatrics and we soon left.

Cindy later told me she had been very down that day, having just been rejected by her lover, and Uncle Sammy gave her the perfect lift. Uncle Sammy not knowing, but knowing, gave her the perfect remedy for her sadness.

CHAPTER 33

The Italians and Opera

Our next-door neighbor's father came for a visit to Hawaii. Jordan was quite concerned about his dad who had just been diagnosed with the early stages of Parkinson's. Mr. Zipoletti, the father, was extremely anxious and depressed. Very soon after he arrived, he overheard Uncle Sammy singing opera. Mr. Zipoletti, who was Italian, loved opera. He came right over to see who the singer was. He was amazed when he saw a very disabled person radiantly and happily singing at the top of his lungs.

After this initial visit, Jordan's father would come over every day and sing opera and Italian folk tunes with Uncle Sammy. He hadn't sung in years, but he loved to sing. Mr. Zipoletti started out timidly, but he soon contacted a long lost aspect of himself and a great source of joy. Since Sammy so easily shared the limelight and was so uninhibited himself, Mr. Zipoletti was encouraged. He, too, began to belt it out. They were quite a pair.

Under Uncle Sammy's tutelage regarding free expression and seeing the transformation of Mr. Zipoletti, I too became inspired. Whenever I drove my uncle anywhere, the two of us would sing *made up* opera and other fanciful ditties in the car. I had a vocal catharsis myself.

Sammy's favorite opera singer, Pavarotti, was on public television one night. Uncle and I sat down to watch and listen. Immediately Uncle Sammy started belting out the song in his usual way. I couldn't hear Pavarotti, so I beckoned to Uncle to *shush*. He looked over at me incredulously and said, "Why, you're ruining my education."

I had to let him sing.

CHAPTER 34

Ancient Wisdom

Often people had no idea what dimension Uncle Sammy was in. People who met him casually never suspected that he had been diagnosed with dementia and deemed legally incompetent.

One afternoon we were in Kailua-Kona, a small town where one could easily walk from one shop to another. Uncle Sammy enjoyed strolling into new shops and engaging with people in his unique style. I was always so curious because these encounters would often have some unexpected twist to them.

On this particular day, we noticed a shop we had never been to. It was called Ancient Wisdom. The shop sold beautiful gemstones, jewelry, and artifacts from different cultures. It also had tarot decks and other items that appealed to people with a certain kind of spiritual perspective, sometimes referred to as *New Age* spirituality. The crystals and other luminous jewels in the window captivated Uncle Sammy. They sparkled and shone, and he was drawn in. I followed.

There were two shopkeepers who were quite friendly. The store had leather couches in the back, and Uncle Sammy headed straight for them. Once seated comfortably, he began to expound on his philosophy. He said, "We've come to donate our happiness, and we want you to be happy, healthy, and dangerous," and began to laugh. Sammy immediately delighted the two women. They sat down next to him, wide-eyed, attentive, and very impressed. They treated him as a very special personage, a *sage* or a *guru* who had just happened to walk into their store. He glowed in the openness and willingness of these women as they sat with him. But he also found their appraisal of him a bit hilarious, and he spontaneously decided to take us all for a ride.

They brought out treats on a tray in little elegant dishes. Also on the tray were beautiful crystals and semi-precious stones. He laughed gleefully and put one of the crystals in his mouth, smacked his lips, and said, "Marvelous!" and then put it down. He played with the other crystals, as the women watched him quite intently. The treats they offered him were vegan hors d'oeuvres. Once Uncle tasted these, he leaned over to the women and said in a stage whisper, "But you know, one of the best kept secrets to life is ice cream. What you wanna do is *do it* and then we have ice cream." The women laughed; they were obviously delighted with these comments because one of the women left immediately and returned shortly with lots of ice cream. There was a very good homemade ice cream shop nearby. We all ate copious amounts of ice cream, and Uncle Sammy became even more animated, with superb one-liners. By the time we left, the women had invited Uncle Sammy to come back to give a talk. He smiled and nodded to them as we left the store and headed home.

Soon Sammy became more physically incapacitated, and couldn't go so far on our neighborhood outings. I, however, would stop into Ancient Wisdom, and the women kept asking me when Uncle could be scheduled to give one of his talks. They persevered in their view that Sammy could be a liberating and inspiring force for others.

What was so delightful to me about this situation was that this inspiration came from such an unexpected source: a little old guy who no longer identified with his name, where he lived, or how old he was. This wisdom came from someone who wasn't a *guru,* and who was, in fact, a part of our population that is seen by our culture as no longer essential, or even functional.

They had never met anyone quite like Uncle Sammy.

CHAPTER 35

Swami Sammy

Power of the Unexpected

After I had lived with my uncle for a while, I realized that he knew things before I verbally communicated to him. I became intrigued. So I began to experiment with purposefully not telling him things in order to find out what he already knew.

On one occasion I was flying to Oahu for the day, and hadn't mentioned it to Sammy. As I was leaving, he winked at me and said, "Happy landing." He already knew.

When I went to an annual retreat, I, again, didn't discuss with Sammy where I was going or what I would be doing. I just let him know that I'd be gone for about a week. Upon returning, my uncle was driven to the airport to meet me by a friend. When he saw me at the curbside he immediately said, "Why, you're a *mystic*." His statement was so unexpected that I landed into a place of wonder. The retreat was, indeed, one based on the mystical path of Sufism.

"What does *mystic* mean to you, Uncle Sammy?" I said.

He replied, "Oh, *mystics* are very keen."

Just moments before I had been reading a book on the plane about developing *keen* awareness.

I began to realize, more and more, that Sammy had an amazing attunement. In fact, friends began to regularly ask him questions about their lives. He became a neighborhood *oracle*, of sorts.

JANET AND SWAMI SAMMY

My sister, Janet, has a great sense of humor, perhaps inherited from Tiger Til and Sammy's side of the family. Janet is *nobody's fool,* she can be of a *doubting* sort of persuasion. Consequently, for the longest time, she did not believe in any of Uncle Sammy's abilities, be they psychic, clever, or other-worldly. She doubted that he had any awareness at all, and thought he made absolutely no sense. Finally, after some years and much accumulated evidence and *coincidences*, she decided there was more to this than meets the ordinary eye. She, in fact, became a *believer,* and took to calling him *Swami Sammy.* She joked with me about putting him to work as an *oracle.*

She would ask periodically, "How's Swami Sammy doing at his new job? Has he made any money yet?"

It became a running joke. One day I told her, "Janet, Uncle Sammy hardly talks at all now." She then suggested: "If he's not talking, tell people that they're getting no response to their questions because they need to purify their hearts, and then return. And you should charge them more!"

We really laughed at this solution.

Finally my sister and I saw eye to eye about our illustrious uncle.

Getting information elsewhere

CHAPTER 36

Getting Information Elsewhere — Hints from the Universe

We all experience synchronicity, serendipity, sometimes called coincidence, which, when recognized, assists us on our life's journeys. Uncle Sammy, because of his ever-increasing, limited mobility, was both more apparent and more awake in his recognition of the hints from the universe, to *Spirit* attuning us. He had a scanning technique for clues. Whatever was in his immediate environment, birds, sunlight, a new day, the color of his socks, magazine advertisements ... all of these clues served to tap into the other dimensions.

While he was still in New York, his many alternative strategies, such as his unorthodox singing and outbursts of sagely advice, were largely misunderstood. His caregivers and relatives thought he no longer made any sense and probably never had. Because of how he was regarded, he attempted to escape his caregivers and had outbursts of anger and frustration. These reactive strategies quickly disappeared when he felt respected.

At times Uncle would be looking quite serious as he was reading, and then I would notice that his book or magazine was upside down. This unusual point of view didn't deter him, however, from getting information, and was part of his technique.

Perhaps his scanning technique was, in part, a result of a disabling condition, his on going mini-strokes. Uncle Sammy had difficulty with word retrieval, yet knew what he wanted to express. He utilized his immediate, external environment to provide for him what his memory couldn't and to access what he needed. The results were often amazingly interesting, and usually had a spiritual dimension. Uncle Sammy was so nimble in what I called his *getting information elsewhere* that his scanning technique caught on. Seeing someone do this with such skill and ingenuity in his condition had a renewing effect on those around him. Friends in his community had great fun comparing notes on the results.

For example, one day Emily was with Uncle when she was looking for auto insurance and comparing prices. Looking at a new car magazine, using his scanning technique, he yelled out, "Bargain," just at the right moment. We had no idea Uncle Sammy was paying the least bit of attention, and yet he was right: the insurance she was looking at right then turned out to be a great deal. On another occasion, when another friend was going round and round, confused about a situation and feeling uncertain, Uncle suddenly yelled, "You be the judge." She had been perusing some legal documents. Again, this proved to be invaluable advice given with perfect timing. Our friend laughed and realized how indecisive she was being.

The title of the book, *Enjoy the Ride* arrived by this *method*.

I'm so grateful for my Uncle's ingenious solutions to his limitations. The pathways he found in order to negotiate his challenges constantly inspired me, and opened my consciousness to new and creative perspectives about life.

CHAPTER 37

Judith and the Unorthodox Sage

Often people who came to visit Uncle Sammy and me knew about his *condition* but didn't know Uncle Sammy. Many people thought they could help out. Most often, *they* were helped out, at least, *out* of their perspective. They would find a shift in their attitude. He was a *Shift-Master*. He changed their gears.

A dear friend Judith came to visit us in Hawaii for a vacation on her fiftieth birthday. She came to celebrate and relax from a high stress job in the financial district of San Francisco. She loved sitting close to Uncle Sammy and rubbing his shoulders. They had several afternoons together, and I heard a lot of laughter.

Judith was easily tickled by Uncle Sammy and has a lively sense of humor herself. On her birthday, as we were celebrating, she asked Uncle to give her some words of wisdom for this period of her life. He said, "On life … Aah … Have very short cares and a healthy appetite! Best to be yourself and relax. That's the important thing. It's unusual advice for you, I know. It just comes up in me."

It certainly wasn't the advice given by the higher-ups in her company. Somehow this really affected her, perhaps because of the energy coming from Uncle Sammy. He had an uncanny certitude combined with his mirth.

While she was visiting, we went to a gathering at a friend's home. It was a beautiful night with a full moon. As it turned out, all the people there were women, and we were inspired to share our aspirations for the months ahead. Before I had left home, Uncle Sammy had said, with great vigor, "Tell those women to double dare." By this time, I had developed a strong curiosity to see if what he had spoken had any bearing on upcoming situations. This was a perfect occasion for this inquiry. As I sat and listened to see if there was a general theme that evening, both Judith and I noticed that it was about courage and daring: daring to be oneself and living out one's dreams.

Later that evening I shared with the women what Uncle Sammy had said. We all had a good laugh, and felt that a little magic was in the air.

Judith and I were especially tickled.

CHAPTER 38

My Dear Child

When I was twelve and my father had just died, my uncle sat with me for hours while I cried, though he rarely cried himself. Sammy, who never went to museums, accompanied me to museums and galleries to support my aspirations to be a painter. Though he didn't have an athletic bone in his body, he went along with me while I ice-skated and roller-skated. He was my second father, and he treated me like his child.

Years later, it seemed like *I* was the parent and *he* was the child, in some respects. He was, indeed, incapacitated when it came to daily chores and care of himself. Yet, he was very wise and self-reliant, emotionally and spiritually. He was an invalid only in the physical sense. In Hawaii he began to show physical affection, and he called me "My dear child."

Day and night and regular hours held no meaning

for my uncle. He would go wandering in our coffee shack whenever he wished. Since there was not much room to wander, he would regularly come into my bedroom, at which time he would sing or ask something. This often happened in the wee hours of the night, because, like a cat, he slept off and on all day and night.

These nocturnal visits had been going on for some time. One night he came into my room quite cheerily at about 3 a.m. and approached my bed. I was not so cheery. Standing right over me he said, in a very loud voice, "I'm S. George Green and where's my brother Ed?" I groaned and said, "Your brother Ed is dead. Now go back to bed!" He did just that. Immediately and abruptly he turned one hundred and eighty degrees, and just as cheerily went back to bed. Most of the time I appreciated his inquisitive nature, amazing revelations, and wise sayings but not in the wee hours. The next morning I put a lock on my door.

When I was growing up my family was extremely oppositional. My mother's mantra was: "Nobody tells me what to do, or when to do it!" Tiger Til, bless her heart, would hang up the phone when she was finished talking, even if the person on the other end of the line hadn't. If you said anything, even if you were repeating what she had just said verbatim, her immediate response was: "No." For example, she would say, "It's hot. This is the hottest summer we've had in years." And I might say, "It's really hot." And she'd find a way to negate what I just said. For a child this was very confusing, and I was never right.

My sister adopted my mother's habit of negation, and since my father was either quiet or absent, this was the family atmosphere. No one was affirmed in this environment of competition. Since this was such a family pattern, never being right, always being told, "No," this deep pattern needed to be healed in me.

When my uncle came to live with me, he was more tender and physically affectionate than he had ever been before. And along with calling me "My dear child," he would say, "You're absolutely right!" to whatever I said. I went from being *absolutely wrong* to being *absolutely right* about everything. This went on for about a year and a half. It became so absurd that, whenever he started to say this, we would both laugh.

Uncle Sammy was keenly aware of whatever needed healing in those around him. Though Janice only took care of Sammy for a brief period, she was definitely in the Union. She was a single mom who brought her young daughter to work with her. Lei, her daughter, never questioned Uncle being in a wheelchair, and would make proper use of it whenever possible. She loved to take Sammy on wild rides in his wheelchair, whirling him round and round, both of them thoroughly enjoying themselves while making sounds of all kinds as they ripped through the house. She was very perplexed, however, when she saw that Sammy had diapers, and that her mother had to change him. I heard Janice explain the cycle of life tenderly to her daughter—that sometimes our Elders become like infants in some ways.

Janice, because of her urban manner and intensity, was very misunderstood in our community. She was labeled *crazy*, and felt quite hurt about this reputation when she heard about it. Uncle Sammy went to work. He started calling her *The Love Song*. He began her new reputation on a day she came to work looking very upset, and he said, gazing at her tenderly, "Why you are a love song." He repeated this as often as was necessary.

Even when someone was deeply upset, Uncle could usually reach them. Kim, a young friend who had grown up in a very disturbed family environment, came to visit. I knew from past conversations that she could often be quite despondent or fearful. Uncle Sammy, with his upbeat nature, simply delighted her.

We had dinner together, and she enjoyed his eating antics. He was so unconventional and unusual in his use of cutlery. One evening, we decided to do some storytelling. After I finished my story, a folk tale from Haiti, Kim began one. It was scary, with demonic figures and sorcery. Uncle Sammy listened, and when she finished he said to her, "Don't worry. I play under ladders." Then he laughed with an authentic, joy-filled laugh. Kim began to laugh, too, and the fear, superstition, and gloom subsided. She then told us that she was coming out of a suicidal period and how amazingly good and carefree it felt to laugh. Sammy said, "You are what I need. I am what you need. But really, you are what you need. All you have to do in life is show up with your own self."

Kim was to leave us a short time later. My uncle said, "You can't leave yet. We haven't got you close enough. You are part of us, and part of our company. Besides, we haven't gotten permission from the 'Union of Beautiful Women.' "

So Kim decided to stay awhile and join our fanciful company, ready to accept her continued healing. Uncle Sammy easily got under her skin. When his conventional pathways of memory altered or dissolved, he had an open channel to *Spirit*.

CHAPTER 39

In with the Union

Terry was one of the main caregivers for Uncle Sammy, and in with the Union. She was a local woman (raised in Hawaii) with a good heart and a hard exterior. All of her life she had taken care of family members. She had also chosen caregiving as her field of work.

Terry was amazingly skilled in her care of Uncle Sammy. Although she was small, she was very strong, and did transfers from the bed to the wheelchair easily, in one, smooth, competent move. I knew this was no small feat, having injured myself transferring my uncle. I admired many of her skills.

Though from very different cultures—she, Japanese-Hawaiian, Uncle Sammy, a Jewish main-lander—Terry was very in tune with his needs, as well as his state of mind. She noticed and adapted to minute and large changes in his abilities.

Her other siblings had chosen professional careers. The incredible skill and sensitivity it takes to be a caregiver was not recognized by her family. I came to learn that her family criticized everything about her, including her choice of work. She was the family scapegoat. Having grown up this way, she adopted this view of herself and her abilities.

After my uncle died, Terry came to our house to help plant a golden tree in his honor, and she told me this story:

"It was on the second day I came to work for Uncle Sammy. I went into the next room to get something for him. Suddenly, I heard him yelling fiercely from his room. It was very loud. I thought immediately, 'Shit. Now what have I done wrong? I'm already blowing it in this situation.' I went to ask him what was wrong and I was very nervous. What I saw was Uncle Sammy laughing uproariously, winking, and pointing at me. I don't know how, but I *got* it, I got what he was doing. He was showing me not to always take the blame, not to feel I'm always wrong and can't do anything right. I'll always remember and thank Uncle Sammy for that." She teared up with gratitude for his easy lessons on Life.

CHAPTER 40

Frances and a Great Fool

I began to get to know Frances, my uncle's sweetheart of more than forty years, after he was diagnosed with dementia.

When my uncle came to stay with me in Hawaii, we returned to New York for two summers, and visited with two important women in his life: Frances and his sister, Tiger Til. After that, he was too physically incapacitated to travel.

During our visit Frances told me that she was relieved Uncle Sammy was in Hawaii with me. For several years she was terrified when he walked around New York, especially when he crossed the streets completely unaware of any danger from either cars or people. I soon got a bird's eye view of this hazard.

One afternoon we all had lunch together at an

outdoor café—Frances, Sammy, Til, and me. Frances and I went inside to pay the bill, and when we came out, much to our horror, we watched Sammy push Til in her wheelchair across Broadway. He was merrily singing and completely confident of a safe crossing. We were not. Cars slammed to a halt. He did indeed make it safely across, in the style of Mr. Magoo, the nearsighted cartoon character.

Years later, after Sammy died, I saw Frances again on a trip to New York. She spoke to me in confidence about their relationship. She said that, although she loved Sammy—he was such a gentleman and so funny—she had been embarrassed by his unconventional ways. She was a bit regretful that she had let this restrict their enjoyment of life together. Frances and my uncle both loved to dance. Yet she felt too embarrassed to go out with him because her friends might consider either his behavior or his attire outlandish, not befitting their company. Frances and my uncle both loved opera. But sometimes she would forego this pleasure with my uncle because of the way he dressed and because he would often leave the performance singing his version of what he had just heard performed. Uncle just wouldn't, or couldn't, modify his ways to meet conventional norms.

When Sammy was gone, she came to realize how many people in her neighborhood had been uplifted by his comedic nature. These people asked about him and missed him. Many different kinds of people commented about how life just wasn't quite as jolly since Uncle no longer came to visit: the elevator operator in her building, the doorman, the grocery clerk, coffee shop employees, and even the man from Kuwait who had a newspaper stand and spoke little English.

She said, "I've reflected on many things your uncle and I experienced. I've come to understand that, although some people thought he was foolish, he was no small fool. He was a *Great Fool*. I've only come to realize this now, both about Sam and about myself, and what drew me to him." She had begun to look for the Greater Story—teachings in life—from this *Sacred Fool*.

Frances was starting to deepen her appreciation of her own soul life and of the being she had spent so many years with.

Maria and Sammy

CHAPTER 41

Older Women

Uncle Sammy's later liaisons with older women were international. At the Day Treatment Center, my uncle met Mrs. Bon, who was an amazing ninety-nine-year-old woman. It was love at first sight. They were each so tiny that they could both fit into one chair. They walked around holding hands until they collapsed into a chair together. Mrs. Bon only spoke Japanese. My uncle spoke no Japanese, and conversed with her using smidgens of other languages he knew: Yiddish, French, Italian opera phrases ... but theirs was truly a language of the heart.

Mrs. Bon passed away just before her one-hundredth birthday. My uncle definitely noticed she was gone. However, it was my sense that he was tuned into the natural cycles of life and death. He dealt with her passing as he prepared for his own: with acceptance and equanimity.

Soon after her death, my uncle fell. Several times before that he had fallen, and I had just put pillows around him where he lay and given him some hot chocolate. He would stay there, happily, until someone else came to help me assist him in getting up. This time I was there as he began to fall, and I injured my own back trying to keep him from falling. Because of my injury, my uncle had to go to a care home until I recovered.

Beverly now owned and operated a small, private care facility in her spacious new home. Both Uncle and Beverly were delighted about their reunion.

Another delightful factor in the equation was that there was a remarkable ninety-nine-year-old Swedish woman who took a swift liking to my uncle. Maria was an exceptionally hard worker, and still gardened and did laundry. She also liked to help with the meals and wash the dishes. She *fell* for my uncle and called him her *boy*. For her, he was a cross between a son and a sweetheart. She tried to get my uncle to assist her, and he did assist in his own way.

They did everything together, or, to be more accurate, she did everything, and he sat and *kibitzed* as she worked. So, while she folded the laundry and they shared the same seat, he would quip in his usual, amusing way, and add to her enjoyment of the task. They were close.

Shortly before her one-hundredth birthday she grew tired and just stopped doing all she did.

A few days before her death, Maria was very cold. Beverly had her wrapped warmly in many blankets. She was in a wheelchair on the lanai, with my uncle in a chair close by. She was contented and at ease. Sammy stayed by her side, and they would look over at each other with acknowledgment. From time to time she would say, "This is so very nice, and wonderful, wonderful." Somehow they were both so comfortable with this process. Like Mrs. Bon, she died peacefully with no struggle and no pain.

My uncle seemed to be surrendering to what life presented. I was about to find out again, he could surrender even in transitions that are extremely challenging for most *normal* people.

CHAPTER 42

Broke Da Hip

My uncle's hip broke while he was at Beverly's. A woman who worked there was helping him dress when the accident occurred. He was taken by ambulance to the local hospital. I was called at home and informed that he could either have their surgeon operate on his hip, or let it be. I decided to speak to the surgeon. In our conversation he said with frail people it's hard to tell which comes first: did his hip break, causing him to fall, or did the fall cause the fracture? He also said it could be a "complicated complication" with someone so elderly. I made the decision to have the surgery, as Sammy clearly had so much life and *oomph* to keep going. Nevertheless, I was really concerned about his undergoing a major operation.

They operated early the next morning. On the way to the hospital following his surgery, I was quite worried. When I entered Uncle Sammy's room he was awake and quite alert. He said, "Come in. Sit down. Be happy." I laughed with great relief. I was astonished at his jolly mood and resilience. My mother, Tiger Til, often talked about the strengths of older folks, and this time I witnessed it. My uncle was in fine spirits. He said, "I had a very complicated complication." Those were the very words his surgeon had spoken, although Uncle had not heard that conversation.

The nurses found Uncle very agreeable, funny, and so entertaining. They told me that as soon as he had regained consciousness he was laughing and joking.

Although his constitution was strong, his veins were not. As often happens with older people, his veins rolled when a nurse tried to put in the IVs he needed. One nurse tried and tried until she had to call in another nurse to assist her. The two of them continued their efforts with my uncle good-naturedly going along with all they were doing. Both nurses suddenly hopped on the bed determined to get the job done. My uncle took them completely by surprise when he said, "Oh baby, get off of me," in a low, sexy voice. He sent them into shocked waves of laughter. His rascal ways were so innocent, yet had outrageous sexual implications. Again, his perfect timing had quite an effect.

CHAPTER 42 • BROKE DA HIP

His overall hospital experience was excellent until we ran into a physical therapist that was prejudiced against Elderly people who were diagnosed with dementia and Alzheimer's. My uncle, who had so much life in him, clearly wanted to keep going with as much health as possible. The physical therapist interviewed him just after his operation, while he still had various medications in him. She asked him complex questions, and she asked him to perform physical maneuvers, both of which would have been difficult for anyone who had just undergone major surgery. She then deemed him *unqualified* for rehabilitation at a facility where they had a physical therapy department. He was eligible for Medicare to pay for this rehabilitation, which would enable him to walk again. I asked my uncle if he wanted this rehab, and he said, "Hell yes!"

My path was clear. I had to advocate for my uncle in the face of this prejudice and opposition. He was not a *throwaway*, and I would not allow him to be treated as such. I went to the social worker and other higher-ups. After many phone calls and much persistence and faith, my uncle was finally admitted to this facility.

When Sammy first arrived at rehab, he looked a bit horrified. The residents had all kinds of disabilities, and it was a very large, long-term institution.

161

Many people would never go home again. After a short while, Uncle began to see them as real people, despite their disabilities. There was one man who had serious congenital handicaps and could only make grunting sounds. At first Uncle looked dismayed when he noticed this man. Shortly into his stay there, Sammy rolled his wheelchair next to this man's and began grunting with him. They developed a close relationship, one in which they clearly liked and understood each other.

The staff was amazingly dedicated. My uncle was eager, and did all the exercises with a great attitude, discipline, and focus. He began to walk, and had great fun learning to walk again. He would put on headphones, and he exercised with music and rhythm. The staff loved him.

There were several women in the facility who Uncle Sammy entertained, and with whom he had friendships. Three of the women ate meals with him. As Uncle Sammy often said, "I have a big responsibility to have fun." And he did have fun, everywhere.

At their table, the ladies watched with fascination while he played with food, completely unconcerned with manners. He could balance food at the end of his knife with great agility. He would load different kinds of food along the knife and see if it made it safely into his mouth. Miraculously, it most often did. He also arranged food by color, and playfully requested contributions of food from the people at his table, in order to make his designs. The residents willingly obliged because the game was of more value to them than the tasteless institutional food.

Sammy was also generous with the outside food that was brought to him, creating a general atmosphere of camaraderie. One of his woman friends said, "Sammy was the sparkle for me here. Don't know how my table manners will be from now on. I feel much freer to step out of my strict upbringing just from being around him."

After three months Uncle Sammy was *liberated* from that institution. Although he had a gift for "livelying up himself" wherever he went, he was ready to come home.

CHAPTER 43

Amazing Contradictions

*'I help the world stay happy,
and things of that nature.'*

People were drawn to my uncle. He exuded such a sense of being completely all right and at ease with *what is*. His external circumstances seemed far from what most would consider ideal, yet his internal world, and thus the way he related to others, was superb. He operated in a vast field of awareness, not trapped in troubling mind activity or judgment, so people felt very comforted in his presence. While appearing to be helpless, he could suddenly rally in service to another's needs, quickly and skillfully.

My uncle was determined to have a specific telephone voice message for anyone who called. It took a very long time to actually record the message, given his physical limitations. The most important part of it was "Hello Beautiful People." He saw everyone through the lens of the *Divine*, and wanted them to see themselves that way.

Besides his major *job*—making people laugh—his other job was getting people to know they are more important and capable than they think they are. He could always see the unique gifts in each person, as well as what held them back. He exercised great craft and craftiness as he conveyed the value of each being to himself. He blessed those around him and eased suffering from his state of grace.

A good friend, Catherine, told this story:

"Sandia was looking for people to work as companions for Uncle Sammy while he was in rehabilitation. My basic job description was to attend to the needs of his spirit. So I was to get to know him as best I could. How would I come to know a man who hardly knew his own name? I came to discover a wise and benevolent person who could appear when I least expected it.

"I was in the process of grieving the break up of a long-term relationship with a man, and I was feeling particularly sad one day. I asked Uncle if he wanted me to read to him. There was a book of Emily Dickenson's poetry on his bed table. He looked at me and said, 'Suuurrre.' So I proceeded. I read two poems and stopped. I said, 'You know, Uncle, I don't really like Emily Dickinson that much. I much prefer Edna St.Vincent Millay.' Uncle paused in his arrangement of the bedclothes, turned to face me, and looked at me quite intently. He said soothingly, 'Everything's going to be okay.' I felt quite clearly that he was seeing what I was feeling, and that he was speaking directly to a deeper place within me. After that experience, I became much more alert to the quality and content of our interactions.

"When my grandfather died at the age of ninety-four, I met my parents in Oregon for the funeral. At the time my grandmother was ninety-three. My father was troubled by the fact that Grandma had dementia, and he was struck with the notion that she had died to him as well. I said to him, 'C'mon, dad, look at her! She's going through a change like we all experience in our lifetimes. This is just a stage where she's letting go of her ego. But her spirit is still there. It's shining through!' I later realized that I had been able to help my father view his mother differently when he sent me an article on "Zen and Alzheimer's" from *Time* magazine, an article that inspired and relieved him. I had the overall feeling that I had positively empowered my entire family constellation.

"To me, my grandmother seemed more alive than ever before. After the funeral I remember her exclaiming, 'Why him? Why did it have to be him? It feels like tears in the back of my head are going to shoot out of my eyes.' It is hard for me to imagine her sharing such a thing before her dementia. I imagine she would have hidden her feelings, drowning them with a few drinks, forcing herself to be cheerful around us. Since the dementia, she spoke out honestly and freely: sometimes directly, sometimes in metaphor, but always truthfully.

"When we would visit her, she would dance about and throw her arms around us when we entered the room, exclaiming, 'My family is here!' I found her authenticity powerful and beautiful.

"I really wonder if I would have seen my grandmother in this light had I not known Uncle Sammy."

CHAPTER 44

The Art of Forgetfulness: Running on Empty

Dementia can be a state of grace. Even though Uncle Sammy forgot the details, he was fueled by divine intelligence. He never forgot the essentials: love, kindness, respect, reciprocity, laughter, music ... though he did forget his name, where he lived, financial matters.

Every morning he greeted the new day and the sun as brand new. I later discovered this to be a practice, worldwide, in indigenous cultures. He, upon awakening, would begin to sing; he never forgot that. He would sing or say in some way: "How lucky the day is! What a beautiful sun it has!" "How lucky the sun is!" or "What a beautiful day it has!" And then he would laugh. With the fresh innocence of a young child, he

A state of grace

would look at his environment and see its beauty as if for the first time. When I walked into his room, he would look at me and say, "There you are!" He was so delighted to see me, as if that was the first time he had ever seen me. We did this every morning.

After being awed by the morning and all of its gifts, my uncle would playfully sing and laugh. He never forgot to play. He was satisfied if I began to sing, too. If I was serious, or if I forgot what was truly important, he would keep on. His intent gaze or a simple gesture would let me know, with no uncertainty, that our morning ritual and meditation had begun. At this point it was irresistible. He shared such joy that I would then remember and join him, playfully singing and laughing, so grateful for the reminder.

After Uncle Sammy moved to Hawaii, he forgot he disliked healthy food. Along with his ice cream and coffee, he ate everything, including salads. After his first year in the islands, he ate with great gusto, and his old worries about overeating, and everything else, were gone. He said, "Don't worry. I never do. And if you don't worry, you don't have to." He completely forgot about worrying.

He also completely forgot table manners, and ate in a most unusual and hilarious fashion. When he ate with friends, they laughed when he encouraged everyone to eat from each other's plates and, most of all, to have fun with their food and each other. He never forgot fun.

Uncle forgot many personal preferences. One of these was his dislike of mustaches. After seeing George's mustache, he grew one, and he loved to fondle and play with it.

He forgot his discomfort with the outdoors and nature. Sammy began to love being in nature, near the ocean. He enjoyed feeling the breeze and the scent of flowers. The beautiful vibrant colors of Hawaii intrigued him, and he would marvel about this beauty. Outer forms, such as personal identity, were forgotten and dropped away. As surface mental activity was forgotten, he could simply *be* in peace and contentment.

CHAPTER 45

Sweet Surrender

'There are only two ways to live your life:
as though nothing is a miracle
or as though everything is a miracle.'

—Albert Einstein

What astounded me most about my uncle was his ability to use whatever faculty remained with great appreciation. Love, joy, and freedom flowed out of his rapture. He realized that every new limitation reveals a new possibility—that "What must be must be." Uncle Sammy surrendered with total grace to the advancing progress of his infirmity.

So often in my professional career as a social worker I had witnessed the shame of people needing help. Sammy suffered no such shame. In deep surrender, he was able to accept all of the physical help he needed with graciousness and appreciation.

When I was injured, my friend Kathleen and her husband, Alan, offered assistance. They transferred Sammy from bed to wheelchair, and changed his diapers. Whenever his diaper was being changed, my uncle would casually put his arms behind his head, as if relaxing at the beach, and allow any and all needed help. Kathleen had been changing his diaper for several days, and didn't think Uncle Sammy took any notice of her or this procedure. Suddenly, one day he looked at her, quite pointedly, and said, "Why, I hardly know you." She was startled into amazement and laughter.

Sammy never identified himself as *a case, disabled,* or *Elderly*. He had little or no attachment to his personal identity, or anyone else's. I once remember saying, "Good morning, Uncle Sammy," and he replied, "I used to be your uncle, but now I'm open to everyone."

He said this in jest, and yet it was accurate. At this stage of his life he was open to everyone he encountered, and had expanded his range of loving kindness.

In his younger years my uncle used his powerful and melodic voice and his love of singing to entertain and amuse. After the onset of his dementia, he used his music for a different purpose: to connect with people, soul to soul, and to open them up. Music and humor were the basic tools of trade for Uncle Sammy's *Crazy Wisdom.*

Over time, with the diminishment of his memory, my uncle would make up songs using different languages, different melodies, and different styles. With his next stage of impairment, he made up sounds, along with some remembered words, melodically, spontaneously, and with much joy.

When his voice no longer had consistent strength, he would seize the times when it did to shock his community into laughter. One Thanksgiving we were at a large gathering at a friend's house with a six-course turkey dinner. Everyone was eating solemnly when Uncle Sammy yelled, "NOW EVERYBODY BACK TO WORK!" completely out of the blue. The energy in the room was transformed, and became much sillier, friendlier and relaxed.

As he lost movement in his lower body, he would gaze admiringly at his hands and say, "Look what my hands can do. Aren't they amazing?"

Later on, he began moving his hands in strong blessing gestures, while speaking the made-up sounds of "ZOOM ZAM ZEEM" or "ZABA DABA DOO." People felt the blessings he sent.

Towards the end of his life, the last year or two, his gestures became gentle and very focused. His glance was potent as he delivered his benevolent blessings. He communicated love, connection, and great joy. He seemed to look into the face of diminished earthly capacities, into the face of death, and not falter.

He was a great model of surrendering to limitations without forgetting the greater opportunities. Not only was my uncle able to surrender to needed help, he surrendered to all the changes life presented. During the entire length of his disabled state, he maintained a great power: that of remaining open and willing to receive whatever gifts the universe provided. Consequently, caring for him became a total joy.

My friend Aerie summed it up when she said, "He was on a surrender bender until he was returned to the sender."

THE JOURNEY HOME

CHAPTER 46

Instructions from Tiger Til

Sometime during her ninetieth year, my mother, Tiger Til, gave me specific instructions regarding her death. While I was visiting her, she said, "Cookie baby, this is up to you. Your sister isn't at all interested. When I die, I want my body cremated. Then I want you to take my ashes out to sea, and as they are being released from the urn, I want you to say, 'Here goes nothing,' " and she laughed heartily. I said "Mama, I didn't know you were a Buddhist." She said, "What's that?" and we laughed even more.

Some years later, when I thought my Uncle Sammy's death was imminent, I started to sob uncontrollably. I assumed I was grieving the loss of my uncle. Later that day my sister called and told me that my mother, who was ninety-seven, had died peacefully in her sleep that morning, at precisely the time when I had begun to sob. Apparently my body knew what my mind did not.

That evening, I began to prepare a giant dinner. I felt great enthusiasm while cooking this elaborate meal. My mind was confused, perplexed. My mother had just died, and here I was doing something I never expected to do on the day of her death. Then I felt my mother's presence, and I received a message from her. She let me know she wanted me to enjoy my body and all of its pleasures as long as I had one. Tiger Til had always loved eating. So I took her advice: I enjoyed her company and finished my meal.

CHAPTER 47

Crossing Over

A few months before Uncle Sammy died, I'd often notice that he was doing his blessing gestures when there was no one in the room with him. As soon as I'd come into his room, he'd say, "There they are!" This was said with the same enthusiasm that he greeted me with each morning when he said, "There you are!" Was he connecting with beings or spirits that I couldn't see or feel? On several other occasions he winked at me, *shushed* me, and began waving again. Uncle Sammy wasn't talking in any recognizable language, though he was clearly communicating. He had a smile on his face, and was actively engaged with someone, or some ones.

This began to happen more frequently. I had been reading about death and the dying process in order to prepare myself for Uncle's transition. Several books indicated that profound teachings, teachers, and messages often come to those who are about to die. Perhaps they come even earlier to those whose consensual minds have left, long before their actual physical death. It was clear to me that my uncle was seeing presences before he died. It was with this knowing that I soon had powerful dreams about his death.

CHAPTER 48

Fly Away Home

I realized Sammy was ready to leave. When I was in earshot he had told a friend:

"She's taking me across."

That statement enabled me to consciously realize that soon I would, indeed, be helping him cross over. I also realized that he knew, and that he was preparing for this passage.

Soon after that incident I had a dream about Sammy and Orion, a young child I am close to. I saw Uncle in his bed, about to die. I was so sad. He seemed to be slipping away into oblivion. Then my attention was drawn to the doorway, and I saw Orion just outside. His aura was all aglow. As he stepped into the room, I looked over at Uncle Sammy and he, too, was all aglow, radiantly preparing to leave his body. This time I felt no sadness, only an awareness of him moving into the light, the next step of his journey.

After the dream I contacted hospice. Hospice sent Ruth, an amazing nurse. She was highly competent regarding the physical changes one went through with strokes and the dying process. She was also very tuned into the spiritual dimension, without imposing her beliefs on anyone else. She arrived and set my mind at ease as much as she could about this great crossing, this mystery. She seemed to know Sammy's essence, although she had just met him. When she returned, she brought her keyboard and she sang to my uncle. She knew how tuned into music and spirit Sammy was. She was one of several hospice nurses who came to visit.

My mother died the day before 9/11, September 10, 2001. One evening, three days after my mom had died, my uncle looked very pale. He had a weak pulse and was struggling to breathe. By 4 a.m. I decided to call Ruth. I was quite alarmed that Uncle might suffer as he passed over. When she arrived, we talked. I realized that I was unprepared to have Sammy leave so soon after my mother's transition. I wanted him to stay. I loved him unconditionally, and he was the dearest person to me. But I didn't want to prolong his life unnaturally. After talking it over, we decided to give him a steroid, which would assist his body in making the transition in a more gentle and easy way. Ruth assured me that the steroid would work so organically that it wouldn't counteract another stroke, or prevent his natural death.

From then on my uncle enjoyed the life remaining to him. We began to call him Sammy Schwarzenegger because he suddenly had enormous strength, especially in his hands, and he also developed an excellent appetite. The hospice nurses began coming around, even when they weren't needed. I got the feeling that it was they who needed to come and be with Sammy. Here was a person for whom the dying process was going well, and who was in a loving atmosphere that supported his journey.

Shortly after that time, my uncle and I were in one of our usual playful conversations. Sammy seemed so very present, and I felt his essence strongly. I was moved to ask if he wanted to stay. He told me quite clearly, "I'm ready to go."

I called Ruth the next day and asked her to come over. From both my intuition, and the conversation of the night before, I knew my uncle's time was drawing imminently close, and she agreed. We talked more about the dying process. She spoke about the last moment, the last breath. Once again, I was more prepared and supported in this sacred process.

On the morning of the next day, Sammy was radiant. Emily had been caring for Uncle, and both she and I noticed how joyous and open he was. I also received direct orders from him. He looked at me and said, with luminous eyes and great love, "You be happy!" He continued to look at me until he knew I got the message.

He ate with great gusto that morning: three bananas, followed by a hearty breakfast, and ready for more. Emily was there to help him that day. When I saw him sitting at the table out on the lanai, resting after his breakfast, I went out to get some supplies. It was then that my uncle left his body.

When I returned, Ruth was there. She told me that Sammy had died. He had just flown away. He had a massive stroke. His head hit the table and he left. It was immediate. Emily had called Ruth, and together they moved him to his bed. When I went in to see him, he seemed as if he was still resting. Intuitively I felt that his spirit had not yet moved on.

That night, I slept with him in his room. I put a pad on the floor next to his bed. Our dog and kitties were there. The kitties usually squabbled about who was to share his bed. But that night they were very peaceful, and both lay across his legs. I never imagined that I would feel the way I did. I was so comfortable. My beloved uncle's presence was still there.

When I dozed off, I had this dream: Uncle was a bit younger, riding a horse on his journey home into the light. As he rode, he got progressively younger until he was a teenager on a bike heading toward the sunset. Then he became a young child, carried in his mother's arms as she ran toward the setting sun. He became an infant. He flew out of her arms, and continued on his journey into the light. My impression was that he was becoming an angelic being, and I felt great comfort from the message and experience of the dream.

I am grateful for the opportunity to have loved my uncle so completely, and I still miss him in so many ways: kissing his rosy cheeks, seeing his radiant blue eyes, laughing and learning from his incredible *Crazy Wisdom*. He comes to me now, but not in those ways. Sometimes I hear his laugh in my laugh. Sometimes I feel his presence spiritually ... a vision, a sound, an energy. Now, I have to be open to the many new ways he can come ...

CHAPTER 49

Mad at Death

For the first several months after my uncle died, I was angry at death. Even though he wasn't fully functional, I felt that, throughout the course of his illness, and perhaps his whole life, Sammy's soul had been refined into gold. He was in a state of perfection to me: affectionate, loving, awake, stationed in the joy of his being. After he had reached this ascendant state, it was almost as if this palpable entity reached out. Death took him.

I had been living with Uncle Sammy for seven years, and for seven years, I was in an expanding state of intimacy and awe. He was my second father, a teacher, a friend, a playmate, and a coconspirator. In all of that time, I never doubted my decision to care for him, and I never resented him. I realize that I was able to have all of the help I needed so that I could also have an independent life, and that was a blessing.

I felt so moved and fortunate to have someone so close to me that I could love so completely.

It took time for my anger to diminish. As my grief lessened, I could feel his presence, which was comforting. And soon I began experiencing visitations and more lucid dreams.

CHAPTER 50

Visitations: Sacred Fun Tradition of the Departed

Initially, I had this belief that if my uncle were to visit me in some form after he died, it would be to comfort me when I was sad or upset. To the contrary, Uncle, in his present form, is still interested in fun, just like when he was alive: his fun, my fun, your fun, the basic joy that is always present beyond circumstances.

The first visitation from Uncle Sammy occurred when I was dancing at the local community center; we both loved to dance. I was having fun, and suddenly there he was. I had a strong sense of his presence, and I heard him give me a message. He assured me he would turn up whenever I was having a really good time. He said that he wanted to help me enjoy myself, and, of course, also enjoy himself. I was surprised. In that moment he was an unexpected visitor.

Since that visit, I feel Uncle's presence whenever I'm joyous. He comes to have fun and to encourage me into new adventures.

Often, just before waking, Uncle Sammy's radiant face has appeared winking at me, reminding me to *lighten up,* and giving me a blessing.

For example, the day I was to buy a car, he came to me in the dreamtime. The gestures and sounds were the same kind that he used to bless me with just before he died. I was able to buy a car with ease. I know his blessing helped.

On another occasion, I was in one of those not quite awake, not quite asleep states when my uncle arrived. It was Sammy, looking like Alfred E. Newman, the "What, me worry?" guy from *Mad Magazine.* He gave me the cosmic wink of a *divine fool.* He was wearing a T-shirt that said, *TRANCES* in iridescent letters that lit up. In the dream I was in a conditioned trance of anxiousness and fear. Uncle Sammy appeared before me, winking and laughing in his glowing T-shirt, rousing me out of my state. In this dream within a dream, I was being zapped with his cosmic laughter once again. He was chortling at the cosmic joke. I woke with a powerful sense of having been gifted.

The third significant dream was luminous and full of love. I dreamed we were in one of the "Dances of Universal Peace," a dance that is about the deepest gratitude for existence. Three people join up and become spokes in a mandala, a wheel of life. The three link arms and bless each other, especially blessing the person in the middle. In my dream, my uncle was in the middle, and he was kissing the cheeks of the people on either side of him, giving out so much love. Of course, they were women. In each kiss was a message about love, about its infinite, boundless, and potent nature. We were about to switch places when I woke up in a sea of that love, feeling held in a state of grace.

I love his visits. They keep me connected to Uncle's spirit, and open me up to knowing something more about the world of the invisible, of the eternal.

CHAPTER 51

Uncle Sammy's Tips for Good Living

After Sammy passed, I had numerous experiences that showed me, again and again, that *Spirit* comes in all forms. Whenever I am in between concepts, free, wondrous, my uncle comes to me: I hear a laugh, feel a presence, my own voice suddenly sounding like his, and I get a *Spirit* message. One of these messages was Uncle Sammy's directive to add these quips and tips to our book.

1. Go from Ow to Wow in the Now.
2. Donate your happiness.
3. Irritate yourself with happiness.
4. Keep going towards happiness.
5. Practice the Art of Forgetfulness.
6. See everything as if for the first time.

7. Bless everything and everyone, and include yourself.

8. Sing everywhere, all the time.

9. Laughter is powerful medicine. Laugh everywhere.

10. Be responsible and have fun! Fun is a great responsibility.

11. Look for allies: they are everywhere.

12. Gratitude is heaven itself.

13. Listen for what makes your heart sing.

14. Choose your trances, and recognize the ones you are in.

15. Give yourself great nicknames.

16. Never let anyone stop you from doing what you love.

17. Don't be stopped from being great.

18. Remember that we are all such gorgeous creatures.

CHAPTER 52

Safe to Die

Our friend, Deanna, a nurse and poet, took care of Uncle during a severe case of shingles after he had taken another fall. She later said, "I was asked to care for Uncle Sammy when he was quite ill with a lot of physical pain. I felt a sense of ease being with him. Even at these times, his most vulnerable times, he didn't seem frantic. As I watched him breathe one night, it occurred to me that I liked Uncle's willingness to go with life's many changes. It was the same when he worsened or improved physically. His body/ mind did not separate from his spirit, and his spirit was strong. I realized that if we were all in tune with our life spirit, we wouldn't resist changes as they arise. Uncle Sammy was a powerful example for me."

Shortly before Uncle Sammy died she wrote this poem:

SAFE TO DIE

TAKE ME TO THE LAUNDRY ROOM AND
    MEND MY HOLY SOCKS

PUT ME IN THE WASH CYCLE, THEN DRY
    ME ON SOFT ROCKS.

LET MY CLEAR LIGHT FLY

AND COME BACK SAFE TO DIE

FOREVER IN YOUR ARMS

ONE LOVE

ONE HEART

                    BIG SIGH

CHAPTER 53

Eleanor and Aerie

Some time after Uncle Sammy died, I became acquainted with my friend Aerie's ninety-six-year-old mother, Eleanor Waters. She had just published her first book of poetry the previous year. She is a very engaging woman who is interested in all spiritual and literary matters.

On some afternoons, I would visit and consult with her about this book. She is so lively and gifted. Eleanor asked me about the book's subject matter, and I said, "It's about my Uncle Sammy and his *Crazy Wisdom*." On hearing that she said, "Put *Crazy Wisdom* in your title," and I did.

She and Aerie also gifted us with a poem. One afternoon, as Eleanor was sitting in her most comfortable chair and Aerie and I were chatting with her, she told us she had begun a poem about Uncle Sammy. She said, "It begins like this ... 'Don't be mistaken, you might think he's fakin.'" Aerie, who is also a poet of the same ilk, immediately contributed the next line: "With his *Crazy Wisdom, you might just awaken.*" Aerie and Eleanor bantered back and forth for a while. Then Eleanor suddenly dozed off, and it was left to Aerie to finish. The entire poem goes like this:

> *Don't be mistaken,*
> *You might think he's fakin'*
> *With his Crazy Wisdom you might just awaken*
> *For deep in the heart of a chuckle or smile*
> *Lies the Truth that hides within many a style*
> *Look deep for that Truth*
> *It can pack a whammy*
> *In the Crazy Wisdom of Uncle Sammy*
> *I may rave 'cuz of how you behave*
> *But seeing your being, now this is freeing!*
> *What I think can keep you hiding*
> *But outside of our mind is Radiant Abiding*
> *So ... Radiantly Abide and Enjoy the Ride!*

CHAPTER 54

Such Good Company

When Sammy died, I remembered how close he and my mother had been, and my mother often saying, "Sammy, he's such good company." So I decided to bring some of each of their ashes to the ocean together.

With my friends Anjahli and George, I had a simple ceremony of prayer for Sammy and Til's ongoing journeys and of thanks for the gifts they had given. The ashes were placed on a boogie board with beautiful flowers. We swam out into a bay called Kealakekua, The Path of the Gods, where they were released. It was windy, and the ashes blew over us as we were in the water. It felt like a very sweet and tender blessing.

My beloved Uncle Sammy has always been such good company for me. I hope he has been good company for you, too, the readers of our book.

Resources

Dementia Support groups online

1. DementiaAdvocacy and Support Network International. DASNI activities currently include an Internet-based support group for people with various dementias and those involved with well-being.

DASNI has an informational and inspiring website by and for people living with dementia: **www.dasninternational.org**.

2. www.dailystrength.org/c/Dementia/support-group

Alzheimer's Online Chat & Support Groups

Many people find online chat groups very helpful. Connecting and communicating with others can be very important for both the person living with Dementia and their loved ones as well. Check for reputable sources.

National Organizations

Alzheimer's Foundation of America

The mission of the Alzheimer's Foundation of America is "to provide optimal care and services to individuals confronting dementia, and to their caregivers and families—through member organizations dedicated to improving quality of life."

Address: 322 8th Ave.,
Seventh Floor
New York, NY 10001
Tel: 866.232.8484
E-mail: **info@alzfdn.org**
Web: **www.alzfdn.org**

External Web Site Policy on such things as diagnosis, treatment, and caregiving go to, **http://www. healthcentral.com/alzheimers** Tel: 312.335.8700 | Helpline: 1.800.272.3900 | TDD: 312.335.5886 | Fax: 1.866.699.1246 E-mail: **info@alz.org** | Web: **www.alz.org**

Websites

There are hundreds, if not thousands, of Internet listings for the diagnosis, treatment, and prevention of Dementia and Alzheimer's. The following websites are reputable as well as informative, and can help you get started. Please note that some website addresses may change over time.

Alzheimer's Association

The Alzheimer's Association is the leading voluntary health organization in Alzheimer care, support, and research. The mission of the Alzheimer's Association is to eliminate Alzheimer's through the advancement of research; to provide and enhance care and support for all affected; and to reduce the risk of Dementia through promotion of brain health.

Address: 225 N. Michigan Ave., Suite 1700
Chicago, IL 60601-7633
Tel: 312.335.8700 | Helpline: 1.800.272.3900 |
TDD: 312.335.5886 | Fax: 1.866.699.1246
E-mail: **info@alz.org**
To find the Alzheimer's Association office & support groups closest to you visit:
www.alz.org/apps/findus.asp

Department of Health & Human Services, Administration on Aging

The Administration on Aging provides home and community-based services to millions of older persons through programs funded under the Older Americans Act of 1965.
Address: Administration for Community Living
1 Massachusetts Ave, N.W.
Washington, DC 20001

Tel: 202.619.0724 | Eldercare Locator: 800.677.1116 | Fax: 202.357.3555
E-mail: **aclinfo@acl.hhs.gov**
www.acl.gov

Area Agencies on Aging, established by the 1965 federal Older Americans Act, receive federal, state, and local funds to contract with local organizations for service to seniors. Each state's agency has a wealth of information and resources for Elder issues, including Alzheimer's and Dementia. To find one near you, in your computer's search engine (e.g., Google) type in "Area Agency on Aging" along with your state's name.

Bright Focus

Bright Focus has a number of links to caregiving organizations that also can be of help:

http://www.brightfocus.org/alzheimers/resources/helpfulorganizations.html#caregiving

eCaring

This is a web-based home healthcare management and monitoring system that enables caregivers to share information with family and loved ones about their patients. "We use the best systems and technology to deliver timely information and effective communications among family members, care managers, and home health providers regarding the daily care and management of seniors and those with chronic conditions."

E-mail: **info@ecaring.com**
www.ecaring.com

Online Information Resource
AssistGuide Information Services

This is an eldercare online resource with a vast amount of information on elder issues, including Alzheimer's and Dementia as well as other conditions, for caregivers and those living with these conditions. It includes a web-based forum where individuals can join in online discussions and moderated conversations.

www.agis.com

Recommended Books

Having Fun with Alzheimer's—A 'How To' Book for Caregivers written by Margaret O'Brien and Michael O'Brien
Inquiries addressed to Paradise Publishing
3400 Hillside Drive
Southlake, TX 76092

MyLifeB4U.com—a not-for-profit site that lets you download the book for free. The authors ask if caregivers have something of value to add, they e-mail it to the authors. This book is an easy to read short guide for caregivers. The authors are a daughter-and-father team their mother and wife respectively had Alzheimer's. They focus on ways to lighten the journey.

Tuesdays with Morrie: An Old Man, a Young Man, and Life's Greatest Lesson written by Mitch Albom. A touching story of the values that can be passed on by the people approaching death; it is also available as a movie.

Mullah Nasruddin Stories. Stories from Persia of a folk character who has classic *Crazy Wisdom*.

Related Links

Doorway into Light.

This is a nonprofit organization dedicated to the spiritual and physical journey of people who are dying, as well as their families, and their communities.
www.doorwayintolight.org and ipuka.org

On the Internet, there are many sites and articles about the benefits of music, music therapy, and the various forms of Dementia.

The Alzheimer's Foundation of America is one great source for this.
Tel: 1-866-AFA-8484
One very good article is found at www.alzfdn. org/education and care/music therapy.html

Poetry and Dementia

There are many articles about the benefits of reading to and writing poetry with people who have Dementia. One such site:

www.ask.com.alzheimers+poems

An interesting article can be found in **agingcare. com** by Susanna Howard who specializes in writing poetry with both people with Dementia and their caregivers. Her system is called Living Words Therapy.

A poem by Mary Oliver
In Praise of Craziness, of a Certain Kind
by Mary OLiver
On cold evenings
my grandmother,
with ownership of half her mind—
the other half having flown back to Bohemia—
spread newspapers over the porch floor
so, she said,
the garden ants could crawl beneath,
as under a blanket, and keep warm,

Sandia Siegel
author of *Enjoy the Ride*
http://www.dimensionsofdementia.com
"Let's Donate Our Happiness"

Questions
for Book Clubs

1. What is the tradition of *Crazy Wisdom*? What is a *Holy Fool*?

2. On reflection, what is your view of the epidemic of the various forms of dementia in our society? How might it be related to our environment, heredity, culture, and biology?

3. How does the Hafiz poem "Tripping over Joy" at the beginning of the book apply to Sammy?

4. Give an example of how Sammy's humor changed someone's perspective?

5. How does the title *Enjoy the Ride* emerge, and what is the significance of the subtitle?

6. Were there instances of Sammy's caring that spoke to you? Were there other instances of caring in the book that spoke to you?

7. What would be an example of Sammy helping someone when they thought they were helping him?

8. How did Sammy care for others with disabilities?

9. What kinds of unconventional behavior would you be comfortable with? Or uncomfortable

with? Would Sammy singing aloud in public or in banks bother you?

10. What qualities did Sammy maintain and what were some of his gifts?

11. How might we appreciate the gifts that someone who is outside the norms of our society still have to offer? (People with dementia, for example, have gone through major transitions and may be quite different than how we once knew them.)

12. How might we learn to appreciate the stories and life lessons of our Elders?

13. How does the idea/inspiration for the book emerge?

14. How did people in Sammy's various communities respond to him?

13. What did you notice about his surrender to his "disability"?

15. What was the prejudice about his dementia that he encountered?

16. In the chapter entitled "What the Hell," Sammy expressed his anger quite directly. What was your response to that chapter? How did Sammy show his anger? Have you reflected further on your own expression of anger or of those close to you?

17. How did Sammy keep his dignity?

18. Who is in the "Union of Beautiful Women"?

19. Were there events in his life when he could have been in danger or in trouble?

20. Which of Sammy's tips for good living spoke to you?

21. Do you remember any other one-liners from other parts of the book?

22. Are there any tips for good living you can offer from your own life?

23. Did any aspect of the book give you a teaching about your own life or about someone important in your life?